BALANCING THE BOOKS

BALANCING THE BOOKS

Financial Problems of Local Government in West Europe

KENNETH NEWTON

SAGE Publications Ltd · London and Beverly Hills

Printed in the United States of America

For information address
SAGE Publications Ltd
28 Banner Street, London EC1Y 8QE

SAGE Publications Inc
275 South Beverly Drive
Beverly Hills, California 90212

British Library Cataloguing in Publication Data

Newton, Kenneth
Balancing the books.
1. Local Finance — Europe
336'.014'094 HJ9417 80-41261
ISBN 0-8039-9802-3
ISBN 0-8039-9803-1 Pbk.

Contents

List of Tables and Figures

Preface and Acknowledgements

In the late Autumn of 1978 the Volkswagen Foundation awarded a research group of the European Consortium for Political Research a grant to produce a report on the financial problems of local government in Western Europe. The idea was not to carry out basic academic research, for this is inevitably time consuming and expensive, and generally results in a long and detailed volume which is read by a small number of academics and specialists before being consigned to the dust of library shelves. Rather, the intention of the Consortium and Volkswagen Foundation was to commission a report which would tackle a problem of current and practical importance, survey the trends, and produce within about two years of starting a report to be written in good, plain English for as wide a readership as possible. The work was to be of the highest academic standards, of course, but it was intended not just for academics but also for practitioners, politicians, and officials in central and local government, and for the interested layman.

The result is this book, which is notably devoid of the usual paraphernalia of academic monographs — footnotes are kept to the absolute minimum, jargon is avoided, complicated statistical and methodological appendices are not included, the argument is laid out as directly and plainly as possible, and each chapter has a brief summary at the beginning and again at the end for the benefit of busy people who want the essence of the findings distilled for them. Those who do not want a short abstract of the argument should skip these sections.

The book covers the post-war developments in six Western European nations — Denmark, Italy, Norway, Sweden, the United

Kingdom, and West Germany. Since the field of study is so complex, and since no one person could possibly grasp the intricacies of more than two or three countries, it was necessary to bring together half a dozen experts, each of whom could call upon a deep and detailed knowledge of local finances in his own particular country, and each of whom was willing to share his expertise with others. The end result, it was hoped, would be a truly comparative report which would enable us to learn from the experience of other countries. This book is based upon the sustained efforts of a research team, each member contributing an enormous amount to the group endeavour. Although the final report was prepared by one person, the real work was done by the other members of the group who collectively prepared no fewer than twenty-five long and detailed working papers, attended a series of five hard working meetings, read and re-read draft reports, checked and re-checked tables and text, and went to enormous efforts to provide tables of statistics which would ensure that the final report was fully integrated and systematic. Collaboration of this kind among academics from different disciplines, countries, and intellectual backgrounds is not at all usual, especially when it demands that a great deal of work is crammed into a short space of time.

The members of the research team were:

Finn Brunn	The University of Aarhus, Denmark
Tore Hansen	The University of Oslo, Norway
Francesco Kjellberg	The University of Oslo, Norway
Guido Martinotti	The University of Turin, Italy
Ken Newton	The University of Dundee, Scotland
Guenther Schaefer	The Institute of Systems Technology, Mannheim, West Germany
Carl-Johan Skovsgaard	The University of Aarhus, Denmark
Jim Sharpe	Nuffield College, Oxford.

The research team took great care to maintain contact with the real world by inviting people with everyday experience of local finances to its discussions. At our meeting in Berlin we benefited from the knowledge of two senior officials from the city's finances office. They wish to remain anonymous. In Oslo, we had the invaluable advice and assistance of Dr. Bernt Lund, the city's Financial Director and a fund of great knowledge and wisdom about city finances. Our meeting at Bellagio was attended by Dr. Ernst Buschor, who is Director of Finances at the Canton of Zurich, and who knows an enormous amount about local finances in Europe. And in Oxford, we had the advantage of the experiences and knowledge of Mr. Maurice Stonefrost, Comptroller of Financial Services of the Greater London Council, and member of the Layfield Committee of Inquiry into Local Government Finance in England, Scotland, and Wales. This study owes a great debt of gratitude to these men who helped to keep its feet on the ground and its head out of the sand.

It is a pleasure to acknowledge the help of academic colleagues in various parts of the world: George Jones, Hedley Marshall, and John Stewart in England; Robert Alford, Michael Aiken, Terry Clark, Roger Friedland, Frances Fox Piven, and Alberta Sbragia in the USA; and those who attended the ECPR Workshop in Berlin in 1977, including Douglas Ashford, Jean Cathelineau, James Danziger, Frans Goudsward, Treufried Grau, Erkki Johanson, Ray Owen, Jan de Lange, and Ira Sharkansky. Among those who helped prepare the detailed working papers John Taylor deserves a special word of thanks for his work on the Norwegian material.

We also owe a debt of gratitude to the Rockefeller Foundation, and to Bill and Betsy Olson, the Directors of the Foundation's Conference Center at Bellagio, who made a truly delightful and productive meeting possible in the Spring of 1978. We would like to thank the Norwegian Association of Municipalities for its kindness and generosity at a meeting of the research group in the Winter of 1977, and the Institute of Political Science, University of Oslo, which was our host institution at this meeting.

Our first and last meetings were held at Nuffield College, Oxford, and much of the work in between was done there. The Warden, Fellows, and staff of the College deserve a special vote of thanks for providing working and conference facilities. At Nuffield, Miss Lynne Remnant typed innumerable memoes, drafts, and letters, coping with references and addresses in a dozen European languages, and handling academic inefficiency with skill and humour.

The final draft of the book was prepared and typed at Dundee where Miss Doris Tindal (the Fastest Typist in the West) managed truly astonishing feats of speed and accuracy in shorthand and copy typing, and where Mrs. Betty Bowman took on the unenviable task of producing the final manuscript in a short space of time. Without them the birth of the final report would have been slow and painful. In the event, it was extremely fast and painful.

And last, but certainly most of all, special thanks are due to the Volkswagen Foundation which funded the project. Jean Blondel and Rudolph Wildenmann, as Executive Director of the ECPR, and Chairman of its Research Board, acted as 'midwives' and catalysts for the study. Without them and the Foundation the study would never have been carried out. In addition, Jean Blondel made many useful comments after his painstaking reading of the penultimate manuscript.

It would be pleasant indeed if the eight members of the research team could claim all the praise and pass the buck of blame. Unfortunately, we have no one to blame but ourselves for any errors of fact and interpretation. As local government finance officers well know, someone must take final responsibility, and this we do collectively, for the book is the product of a truly collective effort.

K. Newton
Dundee, April 1980

Kenneth Newton

is Professor in the Department of Political Science at the University of Dundee. He has published extensively in political science and sociology, and is the author of *The Sociology of British Communism* (1969). He has been Lecturer in Political Sociology at the University of Birmingham; Visiting European Scholar at the University of Pittsburgh; ACLS Fellow at the University of Wisconsin; and Research Fellow at Nuffield College, Oxford

1

Introduction: The Nature of the Problem

Introduction

This chapter describes and analyzes the financial problems of local government in the six nations covered in the study — Denmark, Italy, Norway, Sweden, the United Kingdom, and West Germany — and shows that in these countries, as in most others in the Western world, local government expenditure has increased faster than public expenditure as a whole, which, in turn, has grown faster than GNP in the post-war period. Rapidly increasing expenditure has caused financial problems, severe in some cases, for some local authorities in all countries, and for the entire system in some countries. There are wide variations within any given local government system, but a comparison of the countries shows problems are most severe in Italy, less so in the UK and still less so in West Germany. They are healthiest in Denmark followed by Sweden, and then by Norway. However, local financial problems have worsened over the past decade in all countries, except Denmark, and are generally worse in urban areas, especially in large cities.

It seems as though all our financial problems have ganged up together. Things have been bad in the past, but nothing like this. The wolf is at the door now. To be quite honest, the wolf is at our throats. (Local government official in England)

. . .the towns are on the verge of bankruptcy. . .(French white paper)

The fiscal crisis has currently reached very high levels. Current expenditure on payrolls and basic services greatly exceed revenues from the central government. To overcome this deficit the Milano municipality has been forced to borrow money from banks, further aggravating the imbalanced budget. This has resulted in drastic cuts in investments and operating costs, public employee layoffs and in recurrent difficulties in paying both salaries and interest on bank loans. (Professors Paulo Ceccarelli and Laura Balbo on Milan)

Local authorities in West Germany are faced with their worst financial crisis ever. If they do not get more money from the Federal Government and the Lander, they will have to curtail their services and obligatory expenditure. (Newspaper report)

Single mothers. . .education of retarded children. . .unemployment. . .greater sickness. . .It means that the need to increase taxes is outside the control of local government. That the level of taxation is high and still climbing in Copenhagen and other large Danish cities is therefore primarily due to their great need for services. . .Worse still, if need increases and the tax base is eroded, then taxation must be increased even more. . . (Joergen Lotz, Economic Deputy Director of Copenhagen, quoted in *Socialpolitik*, No. 3, 1978)

In recent years, every commune in the country has witnessed an increasing gap between the supply of finances and the demand for local government services. . .In spite of the fact that local government income has expanded fastest within the public sector, the fact remains that demands and costs have risen even faster. (Bernt Lund, Financial Director of the City of Oslo, in a speech to the City Council, 1977)

The problem

There appears to be something seriously wrong with the finances of the authorities that run our towns and cities. In the past few years, one city after another has run into financial difficulties which range from an unusually severe shortage of funds, right up to full-blooded crisis with the threat of imminent bankruptcy. Rome, New York, Naples, Cleveland, Brussels, Frankfurt, Copenhagen, Palermo, Munich, Liverpool, Tokyo, Milan, and Birmingham have all had to resort to fiscal measures which are more stringent than anything since war-time economies. Other cities join the list as each month passes. If it is not a cut in public services, the cancellation of new plans, or a reducation in the workforce, it is a large increase in local taxes or an equally unpopular increase in charges such as bus fares or rents for public housing. Nor is it just the big cities which are in trouble, for some towns, villages, and rural areas are also facing difficulties.

The financial state of many communes in Italy, for example, is now so drastic that many of them are forced to borrow money at high rates of interest, not merely to pay for new investments, but also to meet current expenses. The local debt has accumulated so rapidly in the past few years that its exact dimensions are now unknown, although it is reliably estimated to total some 33,000 billion lire, or close to 20% of the whole country's GNP. In Rome, local officials talk of the 'monthly miracle' which enables the city to pay its employees and its operating expenses, and to avoid bankruptcy yet again. Meanwhile, the quality of local services is declining as the financial squeeze tightens, not just in the capital city but in many other places as well.

In Britain, local government has been at the centre of a political controversy about the level of local taxing and spending, the quality and quantity of services provided by the cities and the counties, and the very future of the welfare state itself. A series of unusually large increases in local taxes provoked widespread public protests which culminated in a threat by some people to burn their tax demands in front of the town hall. Partly for this reason, and partly because of a growing concern about increases in local expenditure, the government set up a Committee of Inquiry into Local Government Finance. Meanwhile, public spending was reduced and some local services were cut. This provoked a second wave of protests among citizens who bitterly opposed these policies.

In West Germany, municipal finances suffered their worst strains of the post-war period as a result of the recession which followed the oil crisis of 1973. In spite of reforms in 1969, which were designed to give local government more money and distribute it more equitably, city revenues declined with unemployment and reduced business activity. At the same time, the cost of some services increased, and municipalities had to meet greater debt charges as well as the cost of maintaining the capital stock they had acquired during the boom years of the 1950s and 1960s. Local government suffered painfully from cut-backs, which forced a reduction in the quality and the quantity of services provided for the general public.

The situation in France is no better. Some towns and communes have suffered from financial shortage for many years, but in the last decade the situation has deteriorated to a point which causes grave anxiety. In the last twenty years annual per capita expenditure has quadrupled, while capital expenditure has increased sixfold. At the same time, it has proved impossible to cover these expenses with income from local taxes, which has increased only slowly, in spite of big increases in local tax rates. Consequently, local authorities have had to resort to borrowing, and in many places finances are so stretched that they have to arrange new loans in order to pay off old debts.

Some of the major Scandinavian cities have also had to face financial shortage. In Finland, local taxes have increased in real terms by more than 30% over the past fifteen years, and yet municipalities are under such pressure that the use of liquid assets has not managed to avert a steady increase in debts, with the result that local finances are now in a worse condition than any other time since 1945. In Norway, local expenditure and local taxes have risen sharply in real terms over the past quarter of a century, and all Norwegian communes now levy local income tax at the maximum legal rate (22%). At the same time, the amount of local government borrowing, though scarcely critical by British or Italian standards, has become so serious that Ministerial statements have been made about the need to maintain strict control.

In Denmark, the residents of Greater Copenhagen pay local tax bills which are high even by Danish standards, but which are necessary simply to maintain city services at their present level. Even so, Copenhagen has not been able to invest as much as other parts of the country, and public services suffer as a consequence.

It should be stressed that there is often a great deal of variation in the financial health of different cities within the same country, just as there are considerable differences between countries. Nevertheless, local financial problems are widespread enough to be treated as a general malaise which besets many, if not most, nations in the industrialized, Western world. The problem is grave enough to threaten the very future of our towns and cities, and their ability to provide the services which we need and demand — education, housing, social services, public health, roads and transport, fire, police, cultural, recreational, and sporting facilities, and a vast range of other locally provided public services which we all depend upon, but perhaps take for granted until the day arrives when the service is cut. Exactly how serious and extensive are these problems? Is New York the shape of the future? If economically healthy cities continue to spend at the present rate will they eventually come to teeter, like Rome, on the edge of bankruptcy? Should we take draconian measures to avoid disaster, or can we learn from the experience of such places as Denmark and Sweden where financial worries are relatively slight?

The last sentence is an important one which underlines the approach of this work which is essentially one of comparing the present state of affairs, and the histories leading up to them, in six Western European nations. By contrasting the local finances of these countries, each with its own special mix of social, economic, and political circumstances, we can hope to learn something about how and why some countries are able to manage their financial affairs better than others. Only by comparing different countries can we hope to arrive at a sensible understanding of their problems. The rest of this chapter will, therefore, compare the state of national and local finance in six European nations so that we can see the sorts of difficulties they face. It is important to stress, once again, that there are sometimes large variations within any given country: Rome is in crisis, but some Italian communes are better off; many Danish municipalities have relatively few financial worries, although Copenhagen is not in this happy state. But in spite of the differences between cities, there are also significant differences between countries, and it is to these national variations that we will turn first.

The countries covered in the study are, in alphabetical order, Denmark, Italy, Norway, Sweden, the UK, and West Germany. This is not a sample of Western European nations, and nor does it include France or some of the smaller states such as The Netherlands, Austria, Switzerland, and Belgium. The great efforts made to include these nations in the study failed for organizational reasons. In spite of their omission, the six nations cover a variety of economic, social, and political characteristics found among the countries of Western Europe. There is a country with a large population (West Germany with 60 million) and one with a small one (Norway, 4 million), one with a large geographical area (Sweden, with 173,000 square miles) and one with a small area (Denmark, 17,000 square miles), some countries are highly urbanized (the UK and West Germany) and some are less so (Sweden and Norway), some are unitary states with two or three levels of government (the UK and Italy, respectively) while others are federal systems (West Germany), and so on.

Patterns of public expenditure

Table 1.1 gives some details of the wealth and levels of public expenditure of the six nations, and compares them with other Western nations and with their immediate neighbours in Western Europe. It shows that Norway, Sweden, West Germany, and Denmark have high per capita incomes, compared with Italy and the UK which are lower in the league table and below the European average. All six have relatively high levels of public expenditure, although the UK and West Germany are close to the European average. And while public spending is increasing relatively quickly in Norway and Denmark, the rate of growth in West Germany, the UK and Sweden is slower. Overall, the figures show that while the six nations are wealthy and have high levels of public expenditure by comparison with other Western countries, they are not out of line with the Western European pattern.

The figures in Table 1.1 also reveal two tendencies which are fairly general among Western nations. First, high per capita incomes are generally associated with relatively low rates of economic growth, showing that the wealthiest countries have not been able to sustain startling improvements in their standard of living. Second, although the rate of growth has tailed off in most economically advanced societies, public expenditure continues to increase at a fairly rapid rate. Consequently, public expenditure has been consuming a larger and larger proportion of wealth in these countries. Thus, Denmark, Sweden, West Germany, and the UK all have single figure growth rates for the economy as a whole, while Italy and Norway are barely into double figures. In contrast, public expenditure has been increasing at a faster rate, and often in double digit figures of 10, 11, 12 or 13%. The exception is the UK where public expenditure declined marginally as a percentage of gross domestic product.

Table 1.1
Financial characteristics of 21 Western nations: gross domestic product and public expenditure

	GDP per capita 1974, current prices, $1,000	*Public expenditure as % GDP 1974*	*% growth rate GDP 1970-4*	*% growth rate public expenditure 1970-74*
Austria	4.4	38.4	10.7	11.7
Belgium	5.4	37.9	10.2	11.8
Denmark	6.0	47.4	9.7	12.6
Finland	4.7	38.7	13.7	15.4
France	5.1	38.9	10.3	10.5
Germany	6.2	41.4	7.7	10.0
Italy	2.7	—	11.2	—
Ireland	2.2	23.0	12.8*	14.4*
Luxembourg	6.0	44.3	9.3	14.1
Netherlands	5.1	51.4	10.2	13.7
Norway	5.8	48.5	10.1	12.6
Sweden	6.9	49.4	7.8	9.2
Switzerland	7.3	35.8	9.2	11.5
UK	3.4	40.0	9.9	9.3
Canada	6.5	38.6	10.4	12.5
Japan	4.2	24.7	13.4	16.0
Australia	5.9	31.4	12.4	14.7
Greece	2.1	26.7	14.0	13.8
Portugal	1.5	23.0	13.8	12.6
Spain	2.1	23.1	13.9	14.8
Turkey	0.7	—	23.2**	22.2**
OECD European average	3.9			

* 1970-73
** 1970-72

Source: OECD, *National Accounts*, Vol. II, Detailed Tables, Paris: OECD, 1974.

But what of local expenditure? Here the picture is relatively unexplored. Reliable figures for national income and expenditure for the past few decades are plentiful for a large number of countries, but there is no such set of neat and complete tables available for governments below the national level. Comparative work cannot depend upon library sources, but is forced to use research teams of experts each of whom can supply and interpret figures for their own country, a fact which explains why there are so few studies of this kind, and why comparative studies must limit themselves to a handful of nations.

However, figures collected for the six European countries show up one fact very clearly; if public expenditure is rising fast, then local government expenditure is rising still faster. The figures in Table 1.2 and in subsequent tables of this kind, must be treated with some caution, for although every effort has been made to produce a comparable set of figures, it is extremely difficult to do this, given that public accounts, and especially local accounts, are presented in different ways in different countries. It is usually possible to compare the state of affairs in any one country at different points in time, but comparisons across national boundaries are a more difficult task, even when strenuous efforts have been made to standardize accounts.

And yet, even accepting the problem of comparative statistics, the pattern of local expenditure is clear. With the exception of Italy (where the data covers only the 1970-3 period), local government spending is rising faster than public expenditure. In the case of Denmark and Sweden, and to a lesser extent Norway and Germany, the increase is particularly rapid. In fact, the increase may be even faster than the figures suggest, for in some countries, such as Sweden, local authorities have recently sought to avoid central government regulations by establishing 'private' companies, mainly to raise money for housebuilding. Nor do the Italian figures tell the full story, for local expenditure has been increasing more rapidly than other parts of the public sector, with the single but highly significant exception of welfare. Between 1951 and 1973 welfare costs increased twenty times, local costs ten times, and central government costs seven times.

The figures in Table 1.2 highlight one of the problems of local government — rapidly increasing expenditure. The figures in Table 1.3 highlight another problem — that regular sources of local in-

Table 1.2
Gross local expenditure as a percentage of GNP and public expenditure

		Local expenditure as a % of GNP	*Local expenditure as a % of public expenditure*
Denmark	1966	12.4	36.3
	1974	20.1	53.1
Italy*	1970	7.9	32.1
	1973	9.7	30.6
Norway	1950	13.2	45.3
	1974	20.7	52.7
Sweden	1950	10.8	37.1
	1975	23.6	52.6
UK	1950	10.6	30.2
	1976	17.1	33.1
West Germany	1950	6.5	22.6
	1975	9.4	31.6

* Italian statistics do not normally include communal enterprises.

The following constitute the local governments of the six countries:

Denmark	Communes (Kommuner) but not counties (Amtskommuner). Including Copenhagen which is also a county.
Italy	Communes (Communi), and not including the provinces or the regions, unless otherwise stated.
Norway	Communes (Kommuner) but not counties (Fylker). Including Oslo which is also a county.
Sweden	Communes (Communer) excluding the counties (Len). Including Stockholm which is also a county.
UK	Every type of local government unit in each tier of the system.
West Germany	All local governments — cities (Städte), local communities (Gemeinden), and counties (Landkreise).

Table 1.3
Sources of local income:
percentage of gross local income derived from:

		*Local taxes**	*Fees and charges*	*Grants from higher authorities*	*Loans*	*Other***	*Combined local taxes and fees and charges*
Denmark	1950/51	73	4	0****	20	3	77
	1978***	64	10	20****	3	3	74
Italy	1952	57	4	5	24	10	61
	1975	5	0	25	61	9	5
					Loans and other		
Norway	1950	62	21	14	3		83
	1975	52	23	19	6		75
Sweden	1950/51	50	21	15	12	3	71
	1975	45	25	24	6		70
UK	1950	29	14	25	30	2	43
	1976	21	18	44	8	9	39
West Germany	1950	39	16	27	6	12	55
	1973	31	17	27	12	13	48

* Including local shares of national taxes.
** Including income from assets, sale of assets, etc.
*** Budget figures not actual expenditure.
**** Including general grants but not state refunds.

come have not expanded as fast as total spending. Local sources of income have declined as a percentage of total expenditure, but grants from higher levels of government have increased. In some cases the decline in local sources of income has been precipitous — from 61% in 1952 to 5% in 1975 after the tax reform in Italy, for example. Equally, the increase in grants is notable in each country, except West Germany where their proportion of total income has remained constant in the post-war period. It seems that one of the consequences of the rising expenditure of local government has been an increasing financial dependence upon central government. And since local authorities are less and less able to rely upon their own resources, they are also less and less able to determine how much money they will raise and how it should be raised. We will return to this important point later in the book.

A comparison of the local financial problems of the six nations

It is evident even from this brief account that the six nations vary a good deal in terms of their current financial conditions. But how do we go beyond impressions and compare the countries in a careful and systematic manner? Strangely enough, this turns out to be a rather difficult problem, for although it is easy to sort out the extreme cases, those in the grey area in the middle are more difficult. At one extreme there is the crisis of bankruptcy in which local authorities are unable to meet their operating expenses, or to maintain the minimum services which guarantee the health and safety of citizens. At the other extreme, income in excess of expenditure will enable funds to be saved for more adverse times.

Almost any single measure used to assess the situation in between these extremes is likely to be inadequate or misleading, but by using a combination of different measures and indicators we are likely to obtain an accurate picture of the state of affairs in any given country, and to be able to compare and rank one against another. This study uses five measures.

1. *Gross debts*. A city which borrows money may be so pressed that it is forced to negotiate loans to make ends meet, or else it may be so secure that it can afford to run into debt. Oslo recently floated a $50,000,000 Bond issue, but since it has a triple-A rating on the international money market, its Bonds

are as secure as the Kingdom of Norway itself. Indebtedness does not necessarily indicate financial shortage. The steady accumulation of debts, however, is a different matter, especially if these are used to pay off previous loans or to finance current expenditure.

2. *The surplus or deficit before loan transactions.* Like indebtedness, a deficit of this kind may suggest nothing more than a temporary problem, or it may suggest something more severe. A long term, or rapidly increasing deficit is likely to be a good warning sign.
3. *Debt charges as a percentage of total expenditure.* While it may be economically sensible, in some circumstances, to go into debt, debt charges are bound to reduce the money available for current expenditure, and it makes little sense to hand over large amounts of money to creditors, when it could be more fruitfully spent on services.
4. *Real increases or decreases in expenditure.* A fourth measure is the need to cut total spending, or its rate of growth. It is possible that a trend of this kind might be caused by a slackening in the demand for local services, or increased efficiency in their production, but later chapters of this book will show that the overall demand for local services is generally expanding, and is likely to continue doing so in the immediate future. (In this context, the term 'demand' will be discussed in the following chapter.) It is also possible that decreased spending is brought about by increased efficiency, and yet while local government has no doubt tried to improve efficiency, this is unlikely to explain more than a small proportion of the cuts. On the contrary, cuts are likely to have provoked a more determined drive for efficiency, rather than vice versa.
5. *Growth ratio of taxes and grants to local spending.* This measure specially developed for the study by two members of the research team, Tore Hansen and Franco Kjellberg, may be defined as the indexed increase in taxes and grants, which form the bulk of local income in most countries, divided by the indexed increase in total expenditure. It is thus a measure of the elasticity of taxes and grants, and total expenditure. For brevity's sake it will be referred to as the Resource Squeeze Ratio, or R/S Ratio. Thus:

$$\text{R/S Ratio:} = \frac{\text{Indexed increase in the sum of taxes and grants}}{\text{Indexed increase in total expenditure}}$$

> This is an indicator of the local resource squeeze, such that when the ratio is less than one, the gap between expenditure and income from taxes and grants is widening. And although it is only a rough indicator, it has the advantage of dealing with changes over time — of being dynamic. Interpreted in the context of the four other measures, the R/S ratio will help in assessing the state of local finances and their trends over time.

Although none of these measures can be used with certainty on its own to compare and rank countries, all five together allow us to do so with some confidence. The results of the comparison are laid out in Table 1.4, which ranks the six nations according to the severity of their financial problems. Clearly, Denmark as a whole has few if any serious problems at the moment, although Greater Copenhagen is something of an exception. Although it may be hard to conceive for finance officers in some countries, Danish municipalities are generally in the enviable state of having a more than adequate income to cover their current and capital expenditure. Thus, while total spending increased 167% between 1970/1 and 1976/7, total debts increased by a mere 15%. Debt charges fell from 11.6% of current expenditure in 1966/7 to 2.1% in 1976/7. In fact, municipal liquid assets are so great that the central government is worried about their consequences for the national economy, and about the power which municipalities have to charge high rates of interest on the money they lend to private banks. As Table 1.4 shows, all the indicators point in the same direction — taken as a whole, Danish municipalities are in a good financial position.

The situation in Sweden is not quite as good as this, but nor is it much worse. Per capita debts have increased in Swedish municipalities, but they have not increased as rapidly as total expenditure, falling from 106% of total expenditure in 1950 to only 42% in 1975. Loans now contribute less than 5% of total income, and debt interest consumes only 4.3% of total expenditure, although the figure is rather higher in the large towns and cities. While Swedish municipalities have recently been restricted by central controls on capital expenditure, their overall economic growth has continued relatively unabated in the post-war period, and without signs of financial strain. To this extent, they seem to be only slightly less fortunate than Denmark.

Table 1.4
A Comparison of local financial problems: summary table

	Gross debts	*Surplus or deficit before loan transactions*	*Debt charges as a % of total expenditure*	*Real increases or decreases in expenditures*	*R/S Ratio*	*Description*
Denmark	Decreasing	Surplus	Decreasing	Increasing	Good	Excellent
Sweden	Decreasing		Decreasing	Capital expenditure restricted	Good	Very good
Norway	Increasing steadily	Deficit increasing slowly	Increasing slowly	Increasing	Good but worsening	Good
West Germany	Increasing steadily	Deficit increasing slowly	Increasing slowly	Capital expenditures restricted	Adequate but worsening	Satisfactory
UK	Growing but less quickly than total expenditure	Deficit growing	Increasing steadily	Current Expenditures constant or decreasing Capital spending cut	Poor and worsening	Poor
Italy	Accumulating rapidly, until the reform of 1978	Deficit growing rapidly	Increasing rapidly	Cuts in many communes	Very poor and worsening	Critical

Next comes Norway. Here, debts have increased, both absolutely and as a percentage of total expenditure, especially in the rural communes where per capita debts increased twelve times between 1950 and 1974. Debt charges have also risen from 2.7% of total local expenditure in 1952/3 to 9.5% in 1976. In addition the R/S Ratio has moved in an adverse direction in both urban and rural communes. In the years after 1962 the R/S Ratio for rural communes slowly fell until it reached 1.00 (showing that the rate of increase in expenditure was equal to the rate of increase in taxes and grants) for the period 1962/1975. In the urban communes the R/S Ratio also fell until it reached 0.91 for the period 1962/1975. The national government has also imposed credit restrictions on local authorities with the result that their investment programme has been slowed down. Professor Franco Kjellberg summarizes the economic climate in the following way:

> The situation may not be critical according to international standards, but it has become serious enough to elicit ministerial statements that municipal borrowing should be strictly regulated and delimited, and at the same time, resentment is clearly voiced by the municipal authorities in connection with the credit squeeze.

Norwegian local finances are by no means serious, or anywhere near it, but nor are they ideal, and, if anything, they seem to be getting worse rather than better.

Local finances are also deteriorating in West Germany, where they give rather greater cause for concern than in Norway. German municipalities have had to raise more and more of their money from loans which accounted for 5.9% of total income in 1950, but for 11.9% in 1973. In 1952 a quarter of all investment expenditure was raised from loans, by 1973 it was well over a third (36.4%). Consequently, debt charges have also increased as a proportion of total expenditure — from 0.8% in 1950 to 8.3% in 1973. At the same time the investment programme of local government has been restricted (partly because of pressure from the federal government). While it accounted for more than half of total spending in 1964 (53%), it gradually dropped to 42% in 1973. In other words, while capital expenditure has declined as a proportion of total expenditure, German cities are, nevertheless, accumulating debts (though not very rapidly and from a very low figure in 1950) and, consequently, debt charges have also been increasing. Local finances in

West Germany are beginning to show signs of stress, but this is only mild at the present, and not as acute as the next country, the UK.

On all five of the measures listed in Table 1.4 local finances in the UK show a worsening situation. Debts have accumulated, especially short term debts, the deficit before loan transactions has grown, and debt charges have increased as a percentage of total expenditure. A calculation of the R/S ratio between 1950/1 and 1977/8 produces a figure of 0.75, which drops to 0.45 between 1970/1 and 1973/4. After decades in which local authority spending had increased as a proportion of GNP, it started to fall — from almost 17.9% in 1975 to 15.4% in 1977 — as a result of intense pressure from central government. For a time a fall in inflation and interest rates eased the financial situation, but problems are severe once again as inflation, unemployment, and interest rates have risen. Local finances have become an urgent political issue.

Finally, we come to Italy which is almost a case on its own. Although some cities are in a worse state than others, local finances throughout the country are in a rather precarious condition. Debts are accumulating at an alarming rate; compared with a mere 53 billion lire in 1951, the municipal debt was estimated to be a mountainous 33,000 billion in 1977, although no one knows its exact size. This figure amounts to not a great deal less than 20% of the entire country's GNP. Because of the complications and uncertainty surrounding municipal budgets it is difficult to calculate the resource squeeze for Italy but a figure of 0.45 for 1970-1975 is a rough approximate. Communes are increasingly forced to rely upon loans as a source of income. They increased from 54.9% of total income in 1970 to 64.7% in 1975. Debt charges have escalated accordingly, consuming 50.7% of current expenditure in 1970 and 67.7% in 1975. Many communes have been forced to reduce the quality and quantity of their services. On almost any measure one chooses to use, short of bankruptcy itself, communal finances in Italy are in a dire state. However, reforms implemented in 1978 may have allayed the worst effects, although it is too early to tell.

Before leaving Italy, it should be pointed out that local debts in that country, as in most other countries as well, are not the same as debts in the private sector. In the first place, a private business which cannot pay its own way is likely to go bankrupt, whereas the government is likely to consider stepping in to save a local authority from the same fate. At any rate, there is no case of a local government going bankrupt in Italy, or in the other five countries. In the second place, much of the local debt is owed to higher levels of government who are unlikely to drive local authorities to the point of bankruptcy. And in the third place, a large part of the Italian local debt is caused by the need to borrow against money which will certainly arrive in the future, but which has been delayed by a long, cumbersome, and time consuming bureaucracy. The money is there, but it is not actually on the table. In other words, public sector debts are not the same as private sector debts, but they are still a useful indicator of the state of local financial affairs.

A comparison of the financial problems of local and central government

Financial shortage is endemic to all human society. Is local government worse off than other parts of the economy? Is there any reason to believe that local government finds it more difficult to make ends meet than, say, central government, or commercial enterprises? This question is virtually impossible to answer, so far as private sector is concerned. Comparable statistics are difficult to unearth, and even when they appear to be comparable, their implications are usually very different. For example, public sector debts have a different meaning from private sector debts, because the threat of bankruptcy is not the same. But it is possible to compare the financial state of affairs of local and central government, and this is done in a summary way in Table 1.5.

As with local finances, central government finances vary from one country to another. However, thc important comparison from the point of view of this study is not between nations, but between different levels of government, and Table 1.5 suggests some interesting comparisons. In Denmark and Sweden the public sector as a whole has managed to avoid the serious problems which confront governments in some other countries, but, nevertheless, the first signs of mild strain are emerging at the national level in a way that is not characteristic of local government. In short, public finances in both countries appear to be in a relatively healthy state, but more so at the local than at the national level. In Norway, both levels have something of a problem with growing debts, deficits, and debt

Table 1.5
A comparison of central government finances: summary table

	Gross debts	*Surplus or deficit before loan transactions*	*Debt charges as a % of total expenditure*	*Real increases or decreases in expenditure*	*Comparison of central and local finances*
Denmark	Increase 7 times 1966-77	Deficit increasing	Constant	Increasing	Central government has some debt and deficit problem which local government has generally avoided
Sweden	Growing slower than total expenditure	Deficits growing slowly	Small but growing	Increasing	Central government has some debt and deficit problems which are not serious but which local government has avoided
Norway	Growing, but slower than total expenditure	Deficits growing slowly	Growing slowly	Some cuts	Central and local government problems are both mild and approximately the same
West Germany	Growing slightly faster than total expenditure	Deficits growing slowly	Growing slowly	Increasing	Central government's debt and deficit problems somewhat more serious than local government's
UK	Growing but not as fast as local debts	Deficits mixed with surpluses	Declining marginally	Constant after long period of increases	Central government has some problems but local government's are more serious
Italy	Growing but not as fast as local debts	Deficits growing but not as fast as local debts	Approximately constant		Local problems considerably more serious

charges, and this has introduced a policy of some austerity which has put a brake on growing public expenditure. It is in the last three countries where local government suffers worst by comparison with central government. In West Germany, the UK and Italy (particularly in the last two), growing debts, deficits, and debt charges have forced local government to cut back on both current and capital expenditure, and whereas central government also has its financial constraints, these are less severe and have not resulted in such large deficits or debts, or in financial cut-backs of the same order.

A comparison of Table 1.4 and Table 1.5 suggests that the ranking of nations does not change a great deal whether one compares across nations according to the state of local finances, or whether one compares within nations according to the state of local and central finances. Either way, local government in Denmark and Sweden is in a strong position relative to other countries and to their own central governments, while in Britain and Italy local government suffers the most acute strains relative to other countries and their own central governments. Norway and West Germany fit in between, although Norway probably has more in common with Sweden than West Germany. In short, the three Scandinavian nations have the fewest problems whether one uses international or intra-national standards of comparison.

Yet, even this picture is not quite accurate for, as emphasized already, there is some variation between local authorities within the same country, particularly between the largest city governments which have the worst financial problems, and the rest. The causes and consequences of this will be discussed in greater detail in a later chapter of the book, but meanwhile it is worth making the point that many major cities have financial problems, even in the Scandinavian countries. When comparing central and local finances, therefore, a distinction should be drawn between the local system as a whole, and the particular problems of the large cities which are as bad, if not worse, than anything experienced by central government.

Some popular but inadequate explanations

There is no lack of bar room and seminar room wisdom on the

causes of local financial problems. A short discussion with almost any group of taxpayers is bound to throw up a good half dozen explanations. One of the most popular in some countries is that public servants are corrupt and lining their pockets with increasing amounts of taxpayers' money. There have been enough scandals and court cases in these countries to keep this view alive and well, but even so, the explanation does not go very far. In the first place, corruption seems to be rare in some countries, such as Norway and Sweden, where local spending has risen rapidly. In the second place, even in those countries where corruption has been proved, the amounts of money entailed tend to be rather small, at least by comparison with the business deals of Lockheed and others. In any case, the expenditure of local authorities is now so huge that it would take fraud and corruption on scale unimagined in the most outlandish films and novels to account for anything more than a small proportion of it. A mere 1% of the local government bill in the UK finding its way into private pockets would make more than 200 people millionaires overnight. Local costs in Italy may be inflated by corruption, which is probably more widespread than in the other five nations, as they are by clientalism (a form of public patronage), but even in Italy this can be no more than a small part of the total story. Corruption there is in some countries, but it cannot explain more than a minute proportion of total local spending, and, if newspaper impressions are anything to go by, corruption seems to be more prevalent in the private sector where costs have gone up less rapidly.

It may not be greed and corruption so much as extravagance, inefficiency, ineptitude, and profligacy which explains mounting local government costs. It is often said that public officials and politicians are free with other people's money, but are there real grounds for complaint? Most probably not. Those who make the charge forget that the vast majority of businessmen are also spending someone else's money and, in any case, the public sector is rather miserly with its funds in some ways. A visit to a local authority office is likely as not to reveal worn floor coverings, peeling paint, old office furniture and dull, cramped architecture; its private sector counterpart is rather more likely to have carpets, beautiful receptionists, well appointed offices, and managers driving a company Mercedes, Volvo, or Jaguar. Public officials do not usually have expense accounts to take them to lunch or dinner. This does not make them more efficient in their daily business than private sector managers, but nor does it make them any less efficient, and their level of conspicuous consumption is demonstrably more meagre. The simple fact is that research on the relative performance of private and public sectors is rarely attempted (it would be difficult to know where to start) and there is remarkably little evidence to suggest that the public sector is less efficient, or that the private sector would be more efficient in providing services currently supplied by public agencies. It is true that the businessman has his shareholders and his competitors to keep watch over him, but the public official has the no less demanding and eternally vigilant taxpayer snapping at his heels.

More credible is the theory that local financial difficulties are mainly a reflection of the general economic climate, with countries suffering from recession and inflation having to live with a crisis. Yet this does not account for the growing debts and financial shortage of local government in West Germany, where, as everyone knows, the economy sustained a high rate of growth in the 1960s, and then avoided the worst problems of the 1970s. Italy, in contrast, also maintained a high rate of growth in the 1950s and 1960s, and although the country has since run into severe economic problems, the threat which now hangs over municipal finance predates the downturn of the 1970s, and is out of all proportion to it. Sweden's rate of economic growth does not match either Italy's or Germany's and yet here local expenditure has grown much faster (see Table 1.2) with no obvious signs of stress. There is probably a germ of truth in the theory that local financial problems are related to national economic conditions, but there are enough exceptions to the rule to justify the suspicion that the theory explains no more than a small part of the total story.

It has also been argued that local financial problems are of such a scale and caused by such a complexity of local, regional and national factors, that local government cannot possibly solve its own financial problems. Compared with national government, the resources at its disposal are too meagre and its financial capabilities too inadequate. But in contradiction to the theory, Table 1.3 shows that a country with severe problems, the UK, obtains the highest percentage of its income from central grants. In contrast, the countries which have the least problems, Denmark, Norway and Sweden, all rely heavily on locally raised sources of income. Local government, it seems, can solve its own financial problems, and does so in some countries.

Another 'explanation' centres on the idea that local authority spending is 'out of control'. It is not clear quite what this means or how it explains the present situation, although the phrase purports to describe the fact that local authority costs are rising quickly. But as one expert on local finances in Britain explains, to say the expenditure is out of control completely misunderstands how local government finances work. If local authorities had indeed lost control, they could neither fix the local tax rate, nor arrange day-to-day funding, nor do any one of the thousand financial tasks which local officials carry out in the course of the fiscal year. The statement that 'we should bring public expenditure back under control' is usually used by people who really mean 'we should reduce public expenditure'. The statement is not so much an explanation of anything in particular, as an ideological preference about the proper level of public spending. Besides, local government spending may well be under tighter control now than at any time in the past — cost accounting, cash limits, central government surveillance, PPBS, and financial planning have probably contributed to this.

Whatever the causes of the rapid increase in local costs and of the financial problems which they have created, greed and corruption, extravagance and inefficiency, local government's inability to solve its own financial problems, local expenditure being 'out of control', and the general state of economic circumstances, do not seem to play more than a small part in the creation of the current state of affairs. The real causes are more profound and a good deal more complicated. The main purpose of this book is to sift carefully through fact and theory in order to reach a more satisfactory explanation.

Summary and conclusions

The most impressionistic account of the state of local authority finances in a wide variety of Western, industrialized nations is enough to show that some of them are in a grave, even critical state. In part this is because local expenditure has been escalating rapidly over the past twenty or thirty years. In fact, local costs have been increasing even more rapidly than public sector expenditure as a whole and this, in its turn, has been outpacing economic growth in almost all urban-industrial nations in the West. Rapidly increasing expenditure, however, is not a problem if income rises accordingly. But in most countries in Western Europe, local sources of income have not expanded as rapidly as expenditure, and thus local government has had to rely more and more upon central government grants. These have not always been adequate to meet increases in spending and, consequently, many local authorities have resorted to borrowing larger and larger quantities of money in order to cover their deficits. This, in turn, increases their debt charges, which leaves still less money available to pay for essentials, and so the situation deteriorates still more.

Not all local government systems are in financial trouble. While some of them seem unable to extract themselves from the vicious cycle of deficits, loans, and bigger deficits, others are busy reducing their debts, cutting their loan charges, and building up surpluses while, at the same time, continuing with their ambitious capital investment programmes. Moreover, not all those with financial problems are near the crisis point. The phrase 'the international local financial crisis' is often used by politicians, journalists, and academics alike, but a close and careful examination of the figures shows that while the problem is widespread, it is not to be found in every country, and even where it does exist, it rarely reaches full crisis proportions.

The purpose of this research report is to examine the state of local finances in six Western European countries to see what we can learn from those whose financal affairs are in a healthy state. The countries are Denmark, Italy, Norway, Sweden, the UK, and West Germany. In order to compare the circumstances of these nations, a set of five indicators of financial problems is used: (1) the size of the local debt, (2) the surplus or deficit before loan transactions, (3) debt charges as a percentage of total expenditure, (4) increases or decreases in expenditure in recent years, and (5) the Resource Squeeze Ratio, which is defined as the indexed increase in local income from taxes and grants divided by the real increase in total expenditure. In each case, changes over a long period of time are taken into account, for these not only tell us something about current circumstances, but they also indicate the probable direction of future trends.

None of these measures is adequate on its own, but comparing the countries on all five allows us to rank them against each other. There are large variations between local authorities within the same country, but in general Denmark and Sweden are in good financial condition, with debts and debt charges falling, expenditure rising, and no signs of serious financial shortages. Norway is not quite so fortunate but, nevertheless, has few major problems. A little worse is Germany where debts, debt charges, and deficits have been growing and where expenditure, particularly capital expenditure, has had to be cut. Still worse is the UK where spending has been cut in real terms in some authorities because of a fairly severe financial shortage which has been accompanied by rising debt charges and increasing deficits. Worst of all is Italy where some communes are in a real state of crisis. Debts and debt charges are huge, and accumulating at an alarming rate. The deficit grows each year in spite of expenditure cuts and staff reductions.

It is, of course, true to say that financial shortage is found in every society, no matter how wealthy, but a comparison of local and central government finances suggests that the latter suffers more acutely in West Germany, the UK and Italy. In addition, there is some evidence, which will be explored in greater detail in Chapter 8, to show that the larger cities have worse problems than smaller authorities. It seems likely that even the large cities of the three Scandinavian countries have to face up to more severe financial problems than their respective central governments. To this extent the urban resources squeeze seems to be tighter than the local resources squeeze. And, finally on this point, the local resource squeeze seems to have grown tighter in the last decade or so in all six nations, with the exception of Denmark. Even in Sweden, financial pressures have forced cut-backs in some capital programmes, and in all the other countries debts, debt charges, and deficits have grown, while both capital and current expenditure have either been cut, or their rate of increase reduced. In short, the local resource squeeze seems to have grown worse in five of the six nations, and in all of them the urban resource squeeze seems to be worse than in other parts of the public sector economy.

The financial problems of local government are sometimes attributed to the greed, corruption, and inefficiency of local officials but there is little evidence to support these claims. Corruption, even if it existed on a huge and international scale, could not explain more than a proportion of local expenditure, and there is little hard evidence that local government is inefficient. Nor are local financial circumstances simply a reflection of national economic conditions. Problems are more severe in Germany, for example, than in Sweden where economic growth has been rather more modest. Nor is it true to say that local government resources are inadequate to support the demand for local services, for some of the countries with the fewest difficulties rely most heavily upon locally derived revenues. Lastly, it is neither accurate nor helpful to say that local government spending is out of control, for this does not even describe the current state of affairs, and the phrase is usually used by people who mean to say that public spending should be cut.

The real sources of local financial problems, where they exist, are far deeper than these approaches suggest. They have been brought about by underlying trends many, but not all of which are common to a wide variety of Western industrial nations. The next chapter will present a general approach to these problems.

2

The Local Resource Squeeze

Introduction

The chapter outlines a general approach which will help towards an understanding of local financial problems. It argues that although financial scarcity pervades every part of society, local government in some countries seems to suffer acutely because it is caught in a resource squeeze which consists of two sets of strong but opposing pressures. First, there are powerful forces which cause local spending to increase, but second, there are powerful factors which limit local income. The forces which cause local spending to grow larger include: increases in service quantity, for local government is invariably responsible for services the need and demand for which has expanded enormously in the post-war period; increase in service quality, for local government is often at the forefront of attempts to improve public services and facilities; the introduction of new services, for local government is constantly experimenting with new services and new ways of delivering them; the replacement of social capital, for much of this is old, inefficient, and outdated in areas which industrialized early; increases in the cost of services, for local government seems to be highly sensitive to inflationary increases in prices; and the costs of urbanization and urban government, for urban government, especially in the largest cities, seems to be particularly expensive. On the income side, some local authorities suffer from politically sensitive and unbuoyant taxes, from having to raise a proportion of income from fees and charges, which tend to be unpopular and a poor source of revenue, and from the general political sensitivity of local finances which causes the public to be specially resistant to attempts to increase local authority income.

The local resource squeeze

Every society, and every part of society, has to face the problem of scarce resources, but the problem is a particularly acute one for local government in many parts of the Western world. This is because it is caught in the middle of a resource squeeze which consists of two enormously strong but opposing sets of pressures. On the one hand, there are powerful forces which have pushed up the expenditure of local government over the past thirty years, especially in the last decade or so, but, at the same time, there are also powerful constraints on the amount of money which is available to local government to meet its rising costs. The resource squeeze has, therefore, placed local government on the horns of an acute dilemma; it is presented with demands to maintain, or even improve the quality and quantity of its services, but it also has to accommodate demands to minimize its taxing and spending. Whatever it does is likely to provoke an outcry, either those who want better public services, or from those who demand lower taxes, and often from those who want both.

A great complexity of factors contribute to the local resource squeeze. At the most general level there is the fact that governments are no different from any other part of society in suffering from scarce resources, but the scarcity problem for public bodies is of a rather special kind. Buyers in the economic marketplace usually pay directly for the goods and services they consume out of their own pockets, and thus the market makes available to them only what they can pay for. Public goods are not generally distributed in this way, however, and quite rightly, a different set of considerations based upon social justice, equality and need are employed. Consumers do not pay for many goods and services directly, but pay indirectly through taxes and duties of various kinds. Some pay less than others, and some are provided with free services. Generally where fees and charges are levied for services, as they often are by local authorities, they rarely cover economic costs and the consumer is generally subsidized out of public funds. Thus there is always the possibility of getting more than one pays for, and of shifting the costs on to others.

For these sorts of reasons, the public invariably demands more than it is willing to pay for, and hence governments are under continual pressure to deliver more and more, while keeping taxes down. 'In a nutshell', as L. J. Sharpe has put it, 'the public are insatiable consumers of public services but reluctant, not to say hostile, taxpayers. This is the origin of the so-called "resource squeeze" that the governments of all advanced industrial democracies seem to face'.[1]

Local government suffers as much from this scarcity problem as any other level of government, but, in addition, it appears to carry extra burdens which make the squeeze even tighter, and financial strains even more intense. This is because service demands seem to be even more dynamic, while the constraints upon revenue are even more severe. The rest of this chapter will outline the major factors which explain these rather special circumstances. Since the resource squeeze consists of a set of powerful pressures for increased expenditure, combined with another set of pressures which restrict the supply of money, the discussion will consider each side of the income and expenditure equation in turn.

Part I: The Causes of Increased Expenditure

Increased service quantity

It seems that many of the social groups which typically make the biggest demands upon local authorities have increased as a proportion of the total population in many industrial nations. Improved medical care and a higher standard of living have resulted in fairly large increases in the number of old people, and also of mentally and physically handicapped people of all ages. While the responsibility for pensions and social security generally falls upon central government, local authorities have a legal and a moral responsibility for providing a range of amenities and services for the elderly and the handicapped. At the same time the increasing number of working mothers has created a demand for more day care facilities, while the growth of a migrant labour force has created a need for a further range of specialized educational and social services.

Education has also expanded rapidly, not because of increases in the school age population, but because each successive generation seems to require more full-time education. It is likely that the post-war expansion in education has fed upon itself, for the greater number of children who successfully complete primary education, the greater the number who go on to secondary education, and then to further and higher education. And the more education parents receive, the more their children are likely to want. Each generation seems to require the same amount of education as its predecessor, plus another one or two years. In addition, central government has often played a major part in raising the school leaving age, thereby increasing student numbers. Education is a specially large item in many local government budgets and, consequently, any major expansion of the service is likely to have a significant impact on local costs.

Affluence has also brought with it a large increase in the number of vehicles on the roads, and since highways of one sort or another are usually a responsibility of local government (often in conjunction with regional and/or national government), this is likely to increase the cost of road building and maintenance. Affluence has also been accompanied by a range of demands which have contributed to the resource squeeze in a wide variety of fairly small ways, including pressure for more sports centres, theatres, concert halls, parks, museums, libraries and art galleries. More important, a considerable proportion of private expenditure is dependent upon a high level of public consumption — private cars need public highways, and highly trained professionals and technologists require publicly financed institutions of higher education, for example. Indeed, a 'law' first enunciated in the 1880s by the German economist, Adolph Wagner, argues that public expenditure will generally increase as the standard of living increases, and this seems to be no less true of local than other levels and types of government. In fact, it may be even more true of local government which is mainly concerned with various kinds of services, and it is the service industries which tend to grow fastest in economically advanced societies.

Any attempt to explain an increase in the quantity of goods and services provided at the local level must also take account of the possibility that public awareness of these services seems to have increased, partly because of improved educational standards, and partly because the local media seems to have become both more extensive and relatively cheaper, so that increasingly large numbers are exposed to information about local affairs. Local community groups and public participation aimed at increasing the availability of goods and services also seems to have increased steadily over the past decade or so. In addition, local authorities themselves are beginning to present their products to the public in a more consumer conscious manner.

Before going any further it would be helpful at this stage to discuss the important but problematical concept of 'demand', as applied to the public sector. It is relatively easy to estimate the demand for market goods and services of a given price, but public goods are a different matter, for these are often free, or subsidized, or paid for indirectly through taxes. But while it is not possible to estimate supply and demand curves in the public sector, the term may still be applied to the public sector in the same general way that people are said to 'demand' their rights. In particular, three sorts of considerations have the same consequences for the public sector as effective demand has in the private sector.

The first of these covers instances where the public, or any section of it, makes demands by way of petitions, demonstrations, election campaigns, threats, and so on, upon local government. Those making demands may well not pay for the services, either directly or indirectly, but they are making a demand in the sense of making an urgent request which may be backed not by money but by political resources such as voting strength, political skills, access to the media, or to political decision-makers. Political demand of this kind is double edged because it may be concerned with reducing public sector activity or with increasing it, besides which, decision-makers may choose to respond or not to the demand.

The second case covers instances where the general public increases its demand upon public services simply by using them more. The increasing number of vehicles on the roads is a type of surrogate demand which has ramifications for the cost of road maintenance, the need to build new and better roads, and for the costs of associated public services such as police, traffic management, and parking. Drivers of vehicles may not demand such expenditure (although various pressure groups have done so often and loudly), but by driving on the roads they contribute to wear and tear, and hence to maintenance and other costs.

In the third place, higher levels of government may use their legal powers to oblige local government to extend their range, quality, or quantity of services. By raising the school leaving age, for example, national governments all over the world have, in effect, increased the demand for primary and secondary education. Central government regulations may have more force than effective demand since they are often supported by money, in the form of grants, and by the sanctions of the law.

It seems reasonable, therefore, to talk about the demand for local government goods and services provided the term is not used in the narrow, technical sense, but in a more general and conventional manner to cover political demand, demands upon, and the requirements imposed upon local government by higher levels of government. In each of these three cases the effect upon the public sector may be the same as the effect of changes in demand for market goods and services.

Improved service quality

Besides an increase in service quantity, the post-war period has also seen a marked improvement in quality of local services and amenities. Houses are built to higher standards, schools are more spacious, pupil-teacher ratios are lower, social worker case loads are smaller, libraries stock more books, roads are safer, welfare provision better, and so on. The revolution of rising expectations has hit the developed world no less forcefully than the Third World, and it has probably hit local government harder than other levels of government simply because local government is local, and therefore more accessible to the general public, which has forced it to be more responsive to its demands. According to the Italian economist F. S. Nitti, the more democratic and trusted a government, the more the public is prepared to tolerate high levels of public expenditure.[2] This theory may help to explain why local spending has increased more rapidly than national spending.

Part of the improvement in service quality is due to the influence of the increasing number of professional workers such as planners, housing managers, social workers, and others. These professionals not only add to the salary bill, but they are also likely to press for improvements in the quality of the services they provide, and in doing so they may also add to the pressure to spend on expensive capital equipment such as computers, waste disposal systems, residential homes, and the like. It is said that today's capital expenditure on schools or residential homes creates tomorrow's revenue expenditure on salaries and building maintenance, but the process also seems to work in the reverse direction: employ a professional today and he is likely to argue for expensive equipment to help him to do his job tomorrow. Part of the improvement may also be due to the influence of an increasingly large geographically mobile, middle class population which carries high expectations of local services from one area to another.

Better services also result from the movement towards equality and social justice, not only between social groups but also between areas. Tolerance for wide variations in service quality between different regions seems to be diminishing, and this has usually meant a levelling-up of provision in poorer places, with a consequent increase in costs. Central governments usually played an energetic role in this process for they increasingly established a set of minimum standards for a wide variety of services, and then increased their grants to local government in order to cover the increased costs which they have brought about.

New services

If old services have expanded and improved their quality, there is also a tendency for public bodies of all kinds to provide entirely new services. While their extra costs must be off-set against a general tendency for local government to lose some services to higher levels of government, the new expenses are not inconsiderable, particularly in the areas of environmental protection, consumer protection, inner city renewal, pedestrian precincts, sports and entertainment centres, and provisions for special groups such as immigrant workers, handicapped people, and a whole range of minority groups. It is certainly true that the public sector has expanded the range of its activities at all levels of government, but it is also possible that local government has led the field in some respects. Two reasons help to account for this: first, because local government is so close to the people it has had to respond to their needs and demands for new services more quickly than the remoter levels of government; and second, because local government often relates to its clients on a face-to-face basis (in the school, the library, and the community centre, for example) it has tended to experiment with new ways of delivering services to the general public. In other words, local bureaucracies tend to process people, while higher levels of government are more likely to process things, such as roads, houses, or money. Consequently, local bureaucracies may be more sensitive to the needs of people, both in terms of services delivered and methods of delivery. Experimentation of this kind costs money. Moreover, there is a momentum about service provisions; it may be difficult to start up a new programme but once in existence it tends to become part of the established order and to expand. This may induce demand, insofar as the availability of a service may create a demand for it.

The replacement of social capital

Many areas of Western Europe, such as parts of Britain, Belgium and France, were industrialized and urbanized relatively early in the nineteenth century, and, consequently, they now find themselves with a certain amount of antiquated, inadequate, and outworn social capital in the form of old schools, bad housing, and poor roads. Other areas which were destroyed or damaged during the war have also had to spend heavily on reconstruction. The capital loans for this enormously expensive task leave their mark on local finances even now.

The increased costs of services

Another factor which deserves special attention is the rapid increase in costs of many local government services. The inflation rates of the past decade seem to have had a particularly adverse effect on local government finances, partly because local government tends to be both more capital and more labour intensive than higher levels of government. The point here is that a large proportion of central government spending is consumed by money transfers (such as pensions, unemployment and sickness benefit, social security, and so on) and it seems possible that capital and labour costs rise faster than transfers in inflationary periods.

Capital costs have increased mainly because interest rates have risen sharply in recent years. Even if interest rates do not actually keep up with inflation, thus making it cheap or costless to borrow money, the short run effect of borrowing is to increase debt charges, and thus increase the financial burdens of local government. There is also the point that, for many politicians, a loan is always better than a tax increase, and hence the tendency for some cities to go more and more heavily into debt. At any rate, rising interest rates combined with a capital intensity in providing such amenities as roads, schools, and houses have caused an unusually large increase in local government debt charges. Costs will rise still more if, on top of this, local authorities have to borrow to cover deficits on their revenue expenditure.

During inflationary periods there is also a tendency for labour costs to increase more rapidly than other factors of production. The increase seems to be particularly steep in local government. In the first place, it is not possible to switch to capital intensive forms of production in many local government services simply because policemen, teachers, public health inspectors, planners, and social workers cannot be replaced by machines, except to a very limited extent. Second, a reduction in labour intensity may be ruled out by virtue of the fact that service quality is sometimes measured in terms of labour intensity. The quality of education is often judged by the pupil-teacher ratio, that of police and fire services by the number of policemen and firemen per thousand population, and social work by the case loads of social workers themselves. In these circumstances, substitution is likely to be regarded as an attack on the service itself. In other words, many local government services are labour intensive by their very nature, a fact which is reinforced by social and political pressures, with the result that any increase in labour costs is likely to have an immediate and strong effect on service costs as a whole.

It may also be that a relatively large part of local government costs involves the purchase of land and building materials, and that these have increased in price particularly sharply in many Western countries in the past few years.

The last point to be made in this section is the general tendency for public services to become more expensive with affluence and higher levels of technology. It is no longer sufficient to build a swimming pool, ideally it should be Olympic sized, with high diving boards, and a special section for small children. It is no longer adequate to build ordinary roads, they must be carefully designed for safety and capable of carrying heavy, high-speed traffic. It is no longer enough to lay footpaths in the old way, they must have ramps for wheelchairs. It is no longer satisfactory to build theatres, they must have small, intimate auditoria and larger ones with stages big enough for operas and ballet. If the police force consisted mainly of bobbies on the beat, it now involves police cars, two way radios, forensic laboratories and computers. Some of these new developments, such as police cars and radios, may use resources more efficiently, and thereby cut costs, others increase costs, and some may increase them considerably.

The costs of urbanization and of urban government

Another additional factor tending to increase expenditure is perhaps more problematic, but, conceivably, the most decisive of all. This is the tendency in all industrial societies to increasing urbanization and suburbanization which, in turn, increases the costs of local government. It does this in two main ways. Not only are the initial costs of urbanization rather high — sewers have to be put in, roads laid, new schools built — but urban society itself seems to require more government than rural society. Some of these aspects of urban government have already been mentioned in previous sections, but it is worthwhile bringing them all together in this section, if only because they may help us to understand why the financial circumstances of big cities seem to be worse than those of smaller urban and rural authorities.

The differences between urban and rural government can be illustrated by comparing the need for public services of the rural farmer with those of a flat dweller in the middle of a city. The differences between these two seem to fall under three distinct, though closely related, headings. First, the isolated farmer can, at least in theory, provide his own water, sewerage, refuse disposal, vehicular access, out-door recreation facilities, and parking spaces. The flat dweller, by contrast, is likely to depend very largely upon the local authority for these services. In other words, as society becomes more urban, it is likely to increase its public expenditure on services which cannot be individually supplied. These services include such things as water supply, sewerage, refuse disposal, parking and recreation space.

Second, as population density increases so do negative externalities. The economist Mancur Olsen has put it in these terms:

> As population, urbanization, and congestion increase, external diseconomies almost certainly increase too. For example, the farmer in a sparsely settled area who is careless about disposing of his garbage, or who has a noisy household, or who decides to go off to work just when everybody else does, created no problems for anyone else, whereas the same behaviour in a crowded city imposes costs on others.[3]

Olsen goes on to suggest that the number of problems requiring government action is increasing as a consequence of these externalities.

And third, as urban agglomerations increase in size, and as their population densities increase, so they generate needs for collective services which are less pressing in rural areas. These include such things as street lighting, public toilets, traffic signs and traffic lights, pedestrian underpasses, mass public transport, museums, and playgrounds. To this extent the per capita spending of cities on some services is likely to be higher than that in small towns and rural places.

One of the ironies of the cost of urbanization is that it has a further effect on the costs of rural government, for as the countryside becomes depopulated, so its per capita costs rise as it struggles to maintain services at the customary level. Village schools serve a smaller population and tend to become more expensive, social workers have to travel longer distances to reach their clients, and social capital such as roads, sewers, and water pipes have to be maintained even though they serve diminishing numbers. To this extent, not only does urbanization entail costs for urban areas, but it also tends to increase the per capita costs of some services in rural places.

There are three further aspects of the costs of urban government which may not be universal, although they are generally found in larger and older cities. First, there is the extra expense of maintaining services to acceptable levels in the older and larger urban concentrations where worn and inefficient social capital raises running costs, and may be expensive to modernize. Second, there are the sheer diseconomies of scale that arise in the larger cities. It has proved notoriously difficult to demonstrate the precise effects of the diseconomies of scale on city government and, of course, the population threshold where economies of scale are supplanted by diseconomies varies from one service to another. Nevertheless, it is quite probable that the bigger cities do suffer from diseconomies of scale, and that their per capita spending on some functions may be larger, if only marginally, for this reason.

The third possible big city cost is derived from their honey-pot tendency to produce, attract, or retain a disproportionate number of the needy and the deviant, who absorb a more than proportionate share of public services related to housing, social, and health services. At the same time, there is also a trend for the wealthier members of the community to move out of the city. Thus large urban places seem to attract those who are forced to rely on the public sector for some essentials, while they tend to lose those with fewer requirements. Besides, it is often the case that poverty and deviances are more visible in cities than in rural areas, and hence city governments are more likely to respond to social problems, even though they may be more acute than in rural areas.

There is a further set of factors which probably increase the costs of governing large cities; regional capitals act as central places for their hinterland populations, and as such are likely to incur the costs of providing central place services. National and regional capitals often have large public libraries, museums, and art galleries, specialized educational institutions such as universities, centres for technical training and research, and schools for the gifted and the handicapped. They often have municipally financed or subsidized theatres, concert halls, and sports centres. In fact the government of any city is likely to be involved in one way or another with the provision of a whole range of highly specialized services ranging from athletic tracks to zoos.

In addition to the central place services which cities provide or subsidize themselves, they also carry costs generated by visitors and commuters. Not infrequently, and ever increasingly, this amounts to the movement of huge armies of people in and out of the city during the working day, and, for cities like Rome, Paris, Vienna,

Salzburg, London and Edinburgh, even larger floods of visitors. This means business and money, of course, but it is not clear how much finds its way into city coffers, as opposed to the accounts of those who run the tourist trade. Meanwhile, the public sector has to provide services for visitors and commuters. Thus per capita expenditures on such things as highways, police, public health, traffic management, and public transport are likely to be relatively high in big cities.

In general, although with some notable exceptions, urban areas are more likely than rural ones to be controlled by left wing parties or coalitions, and there is some evidence to show that these parties not infrequently spend rather more on some services than their centre and right wing competitors. In Britain, Germany, Belgium, The Netherlands, Italy, France, Norway, and Sweden the evidence suggests that left party control of city councils affects their spending patterns, usually increasing expenditure on redistributive and socially ameliorative services such as social welfare, education, and housing.[4] The effects are not often particularly large, but, nevertheless, they add to the relatively high levels of public expenditure in cities.

And lastly, there is the somewhat paradoxical suggestion that urban areas spend relatively heavily on some services simply because these services are comparatively cheap. Or, to put it another way, some services are so expensive in rural areas that they are provided at a low level or not at all. It might be reasonable to expect a city to organize a fire service which could reach any fire within, say, five minutes. This would be impossible in a large rural area unless very large sums were spent on a huge number of fire stations. Hence rural areas often have part-time and rather rudimentary fire services, while cities have full-time and highly organized ones. It is partly for this sort of reason that rural areas tend to lack public water supplies, sewerage and refuse disposal, libraries, and a range of facilities which require concentrated populations to make them economically viable.

Other factors increasing local government spending

There are two other general factors which may be associated with the rising cost curves of local government. The first is the effects of the local government reforms which have been carried out in most Western European countries (Britain, Sweden, and Belgium, for example) during the last decade. These reforms are generally designed to modernize and rationalize the overall structure of local government and to improve its internal management. In the long run these reforms may well help to keep costs down, but their short run effects may be the opposite, since new structures and processes require an initial outlay to set them up and get them running.

The last proposition on the expenditure side of the local resources squeeze concerns the impact on local spending of different types of central government grants. It has been argued that specific grants encourage local authority spending, while per capita or general grants do not. An authority which can recoup 40, 60 or 75% of the cost of a new school, road, or community centre is likely to take advantage of the bargain, if it can. Danish government has used specific grants in order to increase local spending, although in other countries the effect is not always intended.

Before leaving the subject of central government it is worth emphasizing its part in increasing local expenditure, not only through specific grants but also by imposing minimum standards, levelling-up between areas, enforcing mandatory services, and generally encouraging in one way or another the introduction of new or improved services. The causes of mounting local expenditure are not entirely local — central government is partly responsible as well.

Part 2: Restrictions on Local Government Income

The preceding sections try to explain why local government spending has risen so steeply in the past few years, but they do not explain why this increase has caused such severe financial problems in some countries. Increased expenditure does not present a difficulty if income rises to meet it, and, as we have seen, there are some countries where large spending increases have not caused any undue strain whatsoever. The second part of the explanation of the local resource squeeze must, therefore, examine why local government funds in some countries are tightly restricted, and why the income of some local authorities has failed to keep pace with their expenditure. The four main reasons seem to be the lack of buoyancy of some local taxes, the visibility of local taxes in some countries, the political sensitivity of local financial questions, and the needs-resource imbalance.

The lack of buoyancy of some local taxes

One seldom finds a starving baker, it is said, and one seldom finds a central government with a poor set of taxes. When it comes to understanding why local income in some countries is relatively fixed and inelastic, a good deal of importance must be attached to the distribution of different types of taxes between central and local government. To put the situation in the simplest terms, central government sometimes takes the lion's share of the best taxes, such as income tax, VAT, alcohol and tobacco and petrol duty, and payroll, turnover, and profits taxes. This leaves local government in some countries to depend on a much less satisfactory range of taxes, the worst of which are probably those on land and property. In Britain the property tax is the only local tax. In Austria, Belgium and France land and property taxes are a major source of local income, and in Italy, Denmark, Germany, Norway and Sweden they are minor sources of local income.

One of the main disadvantages of land and property taxes is their lack of buoyancy, by which is meant their failure to keep pace automatically with inflation. The yield of a flat rate income tax increases with any rise in wages and salaries, while a progressive tax may actually outpace inflation because people pay more as they move into higher tax brackets. But land and property taxes are fixed and do not rise with inflation. On the contrary, their yield falls unless steps are taken to revalue property each year, or unless the tax rate is increased. Revaluation each year is difficult and expensive, so in order to maintain real income during inflationary periods it is necessary to increase the tax rate. This invariably meets with strong resistance from taxpayers, who, not unnaturally, think that an increase in the tax rate means a real increase in taxes. In other words, unlike income and many other taxes, land and property taxes are not inflation proof, and it takes an act of political will even to maintain their yield, never mind to increase it. Politicians are often loath to increase the tax rate by more than the essential minimum. The consequence of all this is that the local resource squeeze is likely to be intensified during inflationary periods in those countries where local government relies to a significant extent on land and property taxes as a source of local income.

The visibility of some local taxes

A second major disadvantage of some local taxes, from the revenue raising point of view, is their visibility, by which is meant their propensity to make taxpayers aware that they are indeed paying taxes, and perhaps even the exact amount that they are paying. People tend to be dimly aware that they are paying taxes when they buy goods across shop counters, for the tax is hidden in the cost of the articles. Similarly, income tax is partially hidden because most people pay at source; they have it taken from them before they ever get it. Some local taxes are not painlessly extracted at source in this way. If the taxing authority sends out a bill, and the citizen pays out of already taxed income, and pays in a lump sum, the extraction is likely to be painful. High visibility, intensified by their lump sum nature, makes these local taxes especially unpopular. Hence the saying: pay central taxes in sorrow, local taxes in anger.

Although some forms of central taxation have this lump sum characteristic, a high proportion of central government revenues are not, and by their very nature cannot be, aggregated into an annual total for each taxpayer. The importance of this, so far as it affects public attitudes towards local and central government taxation, can be gauged if all central government taxes (income tax, VAT, alcohol, and tobacco and petrol duty, profits tax, wealth tax, payroll tax, etc., etc., etc.) were added up and the total bill presented to the taxpayer each year. The result would almost certainly be a fierce and widespread taxpayers' revolt, and central government would quickly change the laws so that its taxes became much less visible. This is a disadvantage some local governments have to live with every year when they send out their tax demands.

The political sensitivity of local financial matters

Prudent local authorities will strive to maintain healthy financial balances. However, because local government does not budget for a deficit or a surplus, that is to say it does not, like central government, involve itself in Keynsian management of the economy, its decision-making process is much more sensitive to local tax effects. Local budgets are much more closely related to planned expenditure than central government, and this gives the budgetary exercise a special place in the annual cycle of political events. In fact, the whole question of local taxing and spending seems to be more salient to local than to central government. This is not to say that fiscal matters are unimportant and uncontroversial in central government, far from it, but at the same time, central government's role in creating a surplus or a deficit, plus its inability to calculate either its income or its expenditure in any one year with precision, takes a good deal of detailed budgetary wrangling out of the political arena. Local government, in contrast, can sometimes calculate its income and its expenditure in detail and with some precision, so that a good deal of local political debate hangs upon rather exact financial calculations, so much so that in these countries local financial questions are at the very heart of local politics, and setting next year's budget becomes the very essence of local political aspirations. The political sensitivity of local financial questions may be further heightened by the fact that some countries hold local elections, if not every year, then more frequently than national or regional elections. Consequently, local government in these countries has relatively little breathing space between budgets, and it cannot increase taxes without facing the electorate fairly shortly afterwards.

The importance of local financial questions is further enhanced by the fact that local government in some countries seems to charge for more services than central government, so that a larger portion of its income is derived from fees and charges, rent, and trading surpluses. Increases in these charges to keep pace with inflation places financial matters, once again, at the centre of local political debate. It is sometimes difficult to increase local government charges without creating vociferous opposition, for the provision of services is often regarded as a social duty, and increases in charges are seen as an attack upon those who have to rely upon the state for their wellbeing.

The needs-resource imbalance

The needs-resource imbalance rests upon the fact that the areas which have the greatest need for public services are sometimes the areas which find it hardest to pay for them. In other words, the imbalance exists in particular countries, or in particular areas of them where there is an inverse relationship between needs and resources. In the post-war era this maldistribution may have been enhanced by three related trends:

(i) first, there has been a tendency for industry to concentrate into larger units which, in turn, tends to reduce its geographical spread, thus depriving some areas of a lucrative tax base;

(ii) second, there has been a tendency for commercial and industrial enterprises to concentrate in the wealthiest areas (roughly speaking within the Golden Triangle of the Common Market), and consequently, good tax-base areas seem to have got richer, while poor tax-base places seem to have got poorer;

(iii) third, within the urban concentrations, there has been a centrifugal migration of the wealthier strata from the central city to the suburbs and to smaller towns outside the largest metropolitan areas. Consequently, many cities appear to have lost some of their affluent members while retaining poorer and older sections of the population which often make big demands upon local public services.

Apart from this last trend, the maldistribution of needs and resources is not by itself necessarily related to the local resource squeeze, but it has to be seen against a background of increasing central government and public pressure for territorial equality between local jurisdictions, as well as in the context of general pressures for an improvement in service provision. The trend toward the equalization of life chances between different areas has the effect of reinforcing a competitive and levelling-up process between the poorer and the richer local authorities, so that the former try to achieve the same standards as the latter, despite their narrower tax base. The effect of this competition and equalization is to generate a specially strong squeeze in poorer and needier places.

Summary and conclusions

This chapter consists of a speculative and tentative discussion of the origins of the local resource squeeze. The squeeze consists of two enormously strong but diametrically opposed sets of pressures; on the one hand, there are powerful forces which have regularly and remorselessly pushed up local expenditure, making it rise farther and faster than both public expenditure and general economic growth; on the other hand, there are also forces which place a tight restraint on the amount of money available to local authorities. Thus local financial problems are caused by increases in expenditure being opposed by a less than adequate increase in the supply of money to local authorities. This leads to an examination of the income and expenditure sides of the equation.

There seems to be six main sets of factors which contribute to rising expenditure:

1. Increases in service quantity.
2. Improved service quality.
3. The introduction of new services.
4. The replacement of old capital stock.
5. The increased cost of services.
6. The costs of urbanization and of urban government.

The four major considerations which limit the amount of local income are:

1. The lack of buoyancy of some local taxes.
2. The visibility of some local taxes.
3. The political sensitivity of local financial matters.
4. The resource-needs imbalance.

This list of factors will now become the organizing principle for the chapters which follow. Each of the sections will be considered in turn, and evidence from the six countries will be examined so that we can see how and why the different factors have contributed to the local resource squeeze.

NOTES

1. L. J. Sharpe, 'The Role and Functions of Local Government in Modern Britain', in *Report of the Committee of Inquiry into Local Government Finance*, Appendix 6, *The Relationship between Central and Local Government*, HMSO, 1976, p. 213.

2. F. S. Nitti, 'Principles of Finance', in C. J. Bullock, ed., *Selected Readings in Public Finance*, Cambridge, Mass.: Ginn & Co., 1920, pp. 33-47.

3. Mancur Olsen, *The Logic of Collective Action*, New York: Schocken Books, 1971, p. 171.

4. The evidence to date is summarised in Michael Aiken and R. Depre, *Politics and Policy in Belgian Cities*, Department of Sociology, the University of Wisconsin, Madison, 1977.

3

Increased Service Quantity

Introduction

Local government is responsible for many services the demand and/or need for which has expanded rapidly in the post-war period. This is partly because of an increased proportion of old people, in the numbers requiring health and welfare services, and to increased demand for education and day care services. It is also due to a growing awareness of the needs and demands of the poor, of deviants, and of special and minority groups. There is also the possibility that local government, being more democratic and accessible than other arms of government, has both responded quickly to, and helped to create, popular demand for local services. Central government has added its weight by encouraging spending and by making more money available to local government. Part of the steady climb of local expenditure is also associated with the boom in private consumption in the post-war era, for this has created its own demands upon roads, education, planning, and cultural and sporting facilities. Although education and highways expenditure may now decline, following the falling birth rate and the oil crisis, there seems to be little reason to expect a drop in expenditure for other services, unless, of course, financial problems force authorities to cut their spending.

Methods

The general method used in this and subsequent chapters is to compare the six countries in terms of their service expansion and changes in expenditure for as long a time span as possible since 1950, when local government settled into its post-war pattern. There are many ways of comparing service expansion, of course, but the figures which are most commonly available are the number of service consumers (school pupils, social work clients, beds in children's homes) or the number of service producers (teachers, social workers, firemen). There are also a variety of different ways of measuring service costs — per capita costs, indexed increases, proportion of total expenditure — each with its own special use, and each requiring a different treatment and form of discussion. The measure used most frequently in this study is the change in the proportion of total local expenditure consumed by a given service, for this tells us which services have contributed disproportionately to rising expenditure and which ones have become less important, and thus allows us to pinpoint the causes of increased spending. Local government service responsibilities in the six nations are given in Table 3.1.

Most European societies have experienced fundamental changes in their demographic composition during the post-war period. Absence of war, and an improved standard of living and of medical care have combined to increase the number of old. At the same time, a bulge in the birth rate after the war resulted in a large generation of school children, followed by a new peak in demand for houses when they married to form a new wave of households. Such demographic changes are fundamental to fluctuations in demand for public services, as are other shifts in social patterns, such as the increasing numbers of working mothers, but their effects on local finances vary from one country to another, as we can see from an examination of educational provision.

Education

Education accounts for a large and growing proportion of public sector expenditure (see Table 3.2) and it generally accounts for a large and more rapidly growing proportion of local expenditure. In

Table 3.1
Local government functions in the six nations

	Denmark	*Italy*	*Norway*	*Sweden*	*UK*	*West Germany*
Security, police		L			L	R,L
Fire	L		L	L	L	L
Justice		R,L			L	
Pre-school education	L	R,L	L	L	L	L
Primary and secondary education	R,L	R,L	L	L	L	R,L
Vocational and technical training		R,L	R,L	R,L	L	L
Higher education		R,L			L	
Adult education	L		R,L	R,L	L	R,L
Hospital convalescent homes		R,L	R,L			R,L
Personal health	R,L	R,L		L		R,L
Social welfare	L	R,L	L	L	L	R,L
Welfare homes	L	R,L	L	L	L	L
Housing		R,L	L	L	L	R,L
Town planning	L	R,L	L	L	L	L
Refuse collection and disposal	L	L	L	L	L	L
Arts, culture	R,L	R,L	L	R,L	L	R,L
Parks	L	R,L	L	L	L	L
Sports, leisure	L	R,L	L	L	L	R,L
Roads,	R,L	R,L	R,L	L	L	R,L
Urban road transport	L	R,L	L	R,L	L	R,L
Ports	L	L	L	L		R,L
Airports		L	L	R,L	L	
District heating	L	L		L		L
Water supply	L	R,L	L	L		L
Agriculture, forestry, hunting		R,L	R,L	L		R,L
Electricity	L	L	L	L		L
Commerce		R,L		L		R,L
Tourism			L	R,L	L	R,L

Note: An L (local) or an R,L (regional and local combined) indicates which authorities have at least part of the responsibility for the service, but not necessarily the whole responsibility. The table shows how functions but not financial responsibilities are distributed. In some cases local government is responsible for a function but its total costs are refunded by central government.
Source: Council of Europe, *The Financial Structures of Local and Regional Authorities in Europe,* Strasbourg: Council of Europe, 1976, pp. 41-2.
Functions have changed somewhat in some countries since this table was originally produced, but the overall picture remains much the same.

Italy and West Germany local government spends about a sixth or seventh of its total expenditure on education, and the figure rises to well over 40% in the UK. In general, pre-school and primary education is largely the financial responsibility of local government, secondary education is shared between local and other levels of government, and further and higher education is often the responsibility of national government. This is important for about 90% of public education costs are incurred by primary and secondary levels,[1] and this is precisely where local responsibilities are heaviest. Consequently, even quite small increases in demand are likely to have a significant impact on local expenditure as a whole, and in most cases local education costs have increased not only in absolute terms over the last two decades, but also in relation to other local services.

In two countries, however, Sweden and Denmark, the proportion of the local budget given to education has decreased in recent years. In the case of Denmark the responsibility for secondary schools (gymnasiums) was transferred to regional government in

Table 3.2
Public expenditure on education and the size of the student population

		Public education expenditure as % of GDP (current prices)	*Students as a % of total population*
Denmark	1960	4.0	15.6
	1970	7.0	21.9 (1972)
Italy	1963	3.2	14.4
	1972	4.0	16.3
Norway	1963	5.1	18.3
	1970	6.0	19.4
Sweden	1963	5.0	16.2
	1970	7.1	16.8
UK	1963	4.8	16.1
	1971	5.6	18.8
West Germany	1963	3.0	14.2
	1971	4.2	17.4

Source: OECD, *Public Expenditure on Education,* Paris: OECD, 1976, pp. 10, 12.

the early 1970s, a move which cut the local education bill by a quarter, and virtually doubled regional government's spending on education. In Sweden, spending on education and culture seem to have fallen as a percentage of total local expenditure for two main reasons. First, the local government system has been reorganized around units which were most likely to maximize efficiency in the organizations of primary and secondary education. The number of local authorities was reduced from about 2,500 in 1952 to about 280 in 1974 and the new units were based upon populations necessary to support a comprehensive nine-year education system, thus optimizing economic efficiency for this particular service. Second, the post-war bulge seems to have occurred rather earlier and fallen off rather quicker in Sweden than elsewhere, and consequently educational expenditure reached its peak between 1955 and 1965 and has since been fairly stable.

In the other four countries, however, education costs have risen over the past twenty or thirty years, not only in real terms but also as a percentage of total local expenditure. In other words, the education bill has risen faster than the local government bill as a whole. The same thing is now happening in Denmark, and also in the largest Swedish communes which were not affected by the reforms of 1962, although in neither country is spending back to its previous, higher level. It is easy to see why education costs have increased so rapidly in most countries. It is not that the proportion of school age children in the total population has increased. On the contrary, in all six countries the figures have remained either fairly constant, or have declined since 1950. But the demands upon education in all countries has exploded with expanding student numbers in practically every type of education institution. Central government has done much to encourage and create this demand by raising the school leaving age, by fostering higher educational standards and expectations, and also by taking over an increasing proportion of education expenditure.

The figures in Table 3.2 show the overall trends in education and those in Table 3.3 give more detailed information about local trends. The latter presents information in a rather unusual form, and since it is the first of many in this report, it requires a few words of explanation. Statistical information about different countries is often plentiful, but it is rarely collected or presented in a standard manner which enables it to be organized into a simple

Table 3.3
Education statistics

Denmark				
1st to 7th year pupils	1967:	506,131	1974:	559,745
Secondary school pupils		197,829		283,318
All pupils as % of 1967 total		100		120
Primary school teachers		34,810		62,862
Education as a % of total local current expenditure	1966/7:	20.4	1976/7:	17.7
Italy				
% of total population with high school diploma	1951:	12.0	1971:	27.7
% of total population with secondary school qualifications		5.7		11.3
Kindergarten pupils		940,845		1,619,773
Education as a % of total local current expenditure	1973:	13.1	1977:	14.6
Norway				
Municipal secondary school teachers	1948/9:	1,837	1975/6:	3,947
Municipal secondary school pupils		23,804		66,069
Public primary school teachers		11,500		29,266
Public primary school pupils		300,174		584,897
Vocational school teachers		2,323		6,214
Vocational school pupils		34,425		78,528
Capital expenditure on education as % of total local expenditure	1962	Urban: 3.8	1971	Urban: 4.4
		Rural: 7.5		Rural: 8.0
Current expenditure on education as a % of total local expenditure	1962	Urban: 12.8		Urban: 13.1
		Rural: 20.7		Rural: 22.0
Sweden				
Primary school pupils	1950:	612,155	1975:	1,026,847
Primary school classes		28,846		46,252
Pupils as a % of 5-15 year olds		61.7		89.4
Education and culture as % of total local expenditure		28.6		24.0
— in cities of more than 50,000		17.9		19.8
Local education expenditure as % of total public final consumption expenditure on education	1969:	83.7	1975:	84.0
Total number of teachers	1950:	88,154	1969:	176,892

Table 3.3 (continued)

UK				
Full-time pupils in all schools (mill.)	1951:	5.4	1971:	9.6
Full-time teachers and part-time equivalents	1961:	344,013		477,161
% children taking school meals	1948:	50	1973:	66
School leavers going on to further/higher education		38,000		108,000
Education as % of local current expenditure	1965:	48.1		51.7
Education as % of local capital expenditure		14.4		14.3
Local education expenditure as a % of national education expenditure	1965/6:	83.0	1974/5:	87.2
West Germany				
Kindergarten pupils	1964:	9,000	1971:	50,000
Students in adult education		11,000		29,000
Pupils per thousand population		157		292
Education as % of total local expenditure	1950:	16.2	1973:	15.6

table, such as Table 3.2. The variables are rarely exactly alike from one country to another, and information is rarely collected for the same time period. One is lucky to find any two sorts of figures which cover the same period of years, even within the same country. Therefore, Table 3.3 organizes information on a country by country basis, and specifies the years to which it applies. The format is a little cumbersome, it is true, but the vagaries of international statistics make it impossible to produce anything neater. Nonetheless, the table presents a great deal of information in a readily digestable form. The following national sections draw upon the figures in the table in order to sketch out the national trends.

Denmark

Education accounts for almost 18% of local expenditure on the current account, and although this was higher when local government was in charge of some secondary schools, the figure is now climbing back towards its old level. The Danish figures show the magnitude of increase in pupil and teacher numbers which is general throughout most Western societies — an increase of almost 20% in pupil numbers in only seven years between 1967 and 1974.

Italy

In Italy more and more pupils are staying on at school for a longer and longer period with the result that high school diplomas have more than doubled in the twenty years since 1951. Local government is responsible for only part of the education bill, but this part increased from 13.1% of current expediture in 1973 to 14.6% in 1977. However, demographic changes may mean that education expenditure has peaked, and in the larger cities, such as Milan, there are already surplus school places.

Norway

In Norway education accounts for about a sixth of current expenditure, but the proportion is rising in both urban and rural communes as the years pass. The number of primary school pupils has almost doubled in the post-war peirod, while the number of secondary pupils has practically trebled. The number of teachers has increased more than proportionately to the number of pupils.

Sweden

In Sweden education accounts for rather less than a quarter of total local expenditure and the figure is declining very marginally, although it is tending to increase in the largest communes. While 60% of children attended primary school in 1950, 89% did so in 1975. Over the same period, the number of pupils in technical and occupational schools (a joint regional and local function) doubled.

UK

The UK spends an unusually large proportion of its budget on education by most European standards — over half the current account as compared with a quarter in Sweden, which is the next highest, and only a sixth in Germany, which is the lowest. Local government in the UK is responsible for all primary and secondary education and for a good deal of further and higher education as well. And unlike some countries it shares few of its financial responsibilities with other levels of government, but pays for all teachers and buildings, as well as some student grants. In fact, local government provides no less than 85% of the total spent on education and culture in the whole country. Given these circumstances, it is perhaps surprising that educational costs have not risen a good deal quicker than they have. For example, the number of full-time pupils in all schools almost doubled between 1948 and 1974, a statistic which speaks volumes in itself. The number of full-time teachers increased from 344,013 in 1961 to 477,161 in 1971, and the number of school-leavers going on to further or higher education increased from 38,000 in 1947 to 108,000 in 1971. Until recently almost every age cohort increased its demands upon education, and this has had a highly significant impact on the local education bill.

West Germany

Education accounts for only a sixth of local authority expenditure in West Germany, and even this responsibility is shared with the Lander, which also pay teachers' salaries. Demand for locally provided educational facilities has increased, however, most notably for kindergartens where enrolment multiplied five times between 1964 and 1974, and for certain kinds of adult education (Volkshochschule) where demand in the same ten years increased two and a half times. Local authorities are also responsible for the construction costs of school buildings, and the physical equipment for primary and secondary schools, and, therefore, the costs of a large school building programme in the 1950s and 1960s fell largely upon them, although they were assisted by grants from federal and state government. In West Germany education's share of the total local government bill has fluctuated since 1950, but it has risen steadily from 12.8% in 1961 to 15.6% in 1973.

The immensity of educational expansion in the post-war period has, therefore, added considerably to the financial burdens of local government. The impact has been minimized by reforms in Denmark and Sweden, and maximized in the UK where local government is responsible for finding almost nine out of every ten pounds spent on education in the country as a whole. But in other countries too, education costs are large, and have generally increased substantially during the period from about 1950 to about 1970. However, the birth rate is static or falling in many countries and there are clear indications that the demand for school places is falling. In other words, the upward trend of local educational expenditure may well not continue into the 1980s.

Social services

The public sector is most Western industrial societies is assuming greater and greater responsibility for social welfare, and in most of them this means expanding the obligations of local government which generally play an important role in welfare provisions. In four of the six countries covered in this survey the costs of what are variously termed social welfare, social security, personal social services, or family welfare have increased more rapidly than other local costs. The exceptions are Italy, where local government provides relatively few social welfare services, and Germany where responsibility for some social services has been shifted to higher levels of government, and where a large number of private, non-profitmaking organizations provide welfare services. The welfare system in Germany is extremely complex, and varies from one area to another, but overall, local expenditure fell from 27% of the current account in 1950 to 23% in 1973.

Most local social services are provided for children and old people, and in both cases the general practice is moving away from institutional care in the form of old people's and children's homes, towards preventative social work, community care, psychiatric help, home helps, and home nursing. Consequently, the costs of local authority homes has increased relatively slowly in some countries, but the amounts spent on home and community care has risen

Table 3.4
Welfare services

Denmark				
Social and health expenditure as % of total expenditure	1966/7:	54.0	1976/7:	61.4
Day-care places	1967:	43,187	1975:	134,000
Receivers of public assistance (excl. unemployed)		71,314		141,053
Disablement pensioners		94,448		144,262
Over 65 years as % of total population		11.6	1975:	13.3
Social and health expenditure as % of total expenditures		54.0		61.4
Italy				
Local government provides few important social welfare services.				
Norway				
Day-care institutions	1967:	313	1973:	685
Day-care places		10,200		22,700
Total cost of day-care provision (mill. Kr)		27.4		155
Municipal costs of child welfare	1971:	140		230
Number of social welfare clients	1970:	74,300	1974:	94,230
Average assistance to welfare clients (Kr.)		871		1,106
Beds in old people's homes		18,085		15,939
Municipal home helps		16,106		31,166
Children in care		5,085		9,359
Special schools for handicapped pupils — Pupils	1948/9:	2,389	1976/7:	3,583
Teachers		351		1,186
Total health and social security as % of total local expenditure	1966	Urban: 11.7 Rural: 5.4	1971	Urban: 13.0 Rural: 8.3
Sweden				
Beds in old people's homes	1950:	32,652	1975:	59,892
Beds in local authority children's homes	1972:	2,283		1,524
Places in children's day-homes	1957:	45,036		171,712
Full and part-time home helps	1950:	2,951		4,252
Day-nursery places	1957:	10,510	1976:	76,640
Children in public care	1958:	7,657	1975:	12,018
Social welfare as a % of total local expenditure	1950:	12.2		18.3
% national welfare bill paid by local authorities	1962:	29.9	1975:	31.0

Table 3.4 (continued)

Sweden (continued)				
Pupils at schools for the mentally retarded	1950:	2,297	1976:	13,370
% total population receiving social benefits from local government	1950:	4.2	1974:	5.3
Number receiving social welfare benefits		293,239		436,375
UK (England and Wales)				
Number in children's homes per thousand of pop. aged less than 18	1951:	5.6	1971:	6.4
Number in residential and temporary homes (thousands)	1952:	63.8	1970:	130.6
Registered blind and partially sighted (thousands)		86.8		136.7
Children in care (thousands)	1960:	60.4	1971:	82.8
Local authority social service employees:				
Probation officers	1952:	969	1973:	4,327
Youth officers	1957/8:	351	1967/8:	663
Home helps (thousands)	1959:	23.2	1975:	44.2
Day nursery staff (thousands)		4.6		6.6
Mental health training centre staff (thousands)		1.6		4.3
Social workers (thousands)	1967:	6.0		16.5
Home nurses (thousands)	1949:	5.8	1971:	9.8
Health visitors (thousands)		3.8		6.2
UK				
Local social services expenditure as % of national total	1965/6:	37.2	1974/5:	40.0
Local social services expenditure as % of local revenue expenditure	1964/5:	3.2	1973/4:	5.5

by leaps and bounds. In Sweden, for example, the number of places in old people's homes has risen only a little in the past few years, while in Norway it has actually decreased (see Table 3.4). But in Norway the number of home helps has almost doubled in less than a decade, and the municipal costs of child welfare, preventative care, and after-care has been rising at an average of about 20% per annum over the past few years. In Britain, a similar shift in social work practice to non-residential care has caused an appreciable rise in the number of children under supervision while living at home or with foster parents. At the same time, the numbers in children's homes rose from 5.6 per thousand aged less than 18 in 1951, to 6.4 per thousand in 1971.

In Denmark and Norway, day-care facilities are also local responsibilities which are included in the welfare budget. In the former, numbers using municipal day-centre facilities have almost tripled from 48,000 in 1966 to 134,000 in 1975, and the figure is expected to reach little short of a quarter of a million by 1980. Day nurseries and pre-school provision are particularly expensive in Denmark, as in many other countries, because they demand a high proportion of staff to children. In Norway, the use of day-care facilities has also shot up — from 10,000 in 1967 to 23,000 in 1973. Consequently, day-care spending jumped from 27 to 155 million kroner in the same period.

At the other end of the age scale, the proportion of old people has increased in all six countries, substantially in some cases (see Table 3.5). In most cases central and regional government carries the costs of medical care and pensions, but local government also has responsibilities for the aged, although the nature and extent of these vary from one country to another. In Norway, the number of hospital beds for the aged has increased, and home helps for the elderly have more than doubled since 1970. In other countries, such as Denmark, Sweden, and the UK the number of places in old people's homes has increased as well as the number of home helps and home nurses. Consequently, the costs of old people's services in most countries has risen steeply in the post-war period, and there is every reason to believe that the trend will continue as the population continues to age.

More generally, the economic dependency rate is also rising (see Table 3.5). This rate measures the number of economically inactive people per hundred who are active. Of course, not all economically inactive people require public services, and central government produces many of those they do need, but local government also provides services for this section of the population, and seems to be doing so on an ever increasing scale — not just schools for the young and facilities for the old, but also community centres for teenagers,

Table 3.5
The old and dependent population

	% of people aged 65 or over		*Dependency rate***	
Denmark	1960	10.5	1965	120.8
	1970	13.3	1975	116.3
Italy	1961	9.5	1965	150.2
	1971	11.3	1975	177.8
Norway*	1960	6.9	1965	Not
	1970	9.2	1975	available
Sweden	1950	10.1	1965	107.6
	1975	15.2	1975	109.3
UK	1951	10.9	1965	109.3
	1971	13.2	1975	122.0
West Germany	1950	9.4	1965	116.2
	1974	14.3	1975	134.8

* % aged 70 and over
** The number of economically inactive people per 100 active.

Source: OECD, *Demographic Trends 1970-1985,* Paris: OECD, 1974, Table 11.12, pp. 106-7.

clinics and social centres for young mothers, and special facilities for the handicapped.

There has also been a growing demand for services for special social groups and minorities. Immigrant workers started flowing into Germany in the early 1950s, and gradually increased to form some 7% of the total population in 1975. The majority are of working age and probably pay more in taxes than they receive in services, but, nonetheless, they have had an impact on local service demand, particularly for special education for non-German speaking children. This has been a special problem in the large cities where immigrant workers have concentrated. Much the same has occurred in Britain where immigrant workers have settled in some of the large cities, and where special educational and social facilities have been created for them.

There are many other minority groups whose needs and demands are beginning to be recognized in a wide variety of countries. For example, financial assistance given by Norwegian communes to alcoholics and their families more than doubled in the six years between 1972 and 1977. German municipalities are also making greater efforts to provide treatment centres and counselling services for drug addicts, following an increase in the number of drug deaths. And aid to juvenile delinquents in Germany has increased from 9% to 19% of social services expenditure, 1950-1973. Although there is only scattered information on costs, the general impression is that local authorities in most countries are contributing steadily increasing amounts of money, either directly through their own services, or indirectly through private agencies and charities, towards the assistance of such groups as the mentally and physically handicapped, the mentally ill, mistreated wives and children, and single parent families. As societies become increasingly aware of the special problems of these, and a whole range of other disadvantaged and minority groups, so costs are likely to mount.

Roads and public transport

In the early part of the century it was believed that the need for state activity in many areas of life would decline as the standard of living rose. As the century progressed, it became obvious that public expenditure was not declining but, on the contrary, was increasing at an even faster rate. It is now clear that far from reducing the public sector, growing affluence creates renewed demands upon public goods and services — for education, recreation, planning, social services, environmental protection, and so on. This is, perhaps, most evident in the provision of roads and public transport, for as the number of vehicles on the roads increases, as people travel further and further for work and pleasure, and as more and more goods are carried longer and longer distances by trucks, so the costs of road building and maintenance, and of public transport rise steeply. Rather than competing with the private sector, as many critics of public activity contend, the two complement each other. To take one small example, the boom in second homes has created a demand for more and better roads, and more local planning.

In most countries the heavy costs of building and maintaining public highways is shared between local and other levels of government, but local authorities usually carry a good proportion of the financial burden. A major exception is Denmark where, as with secondary education, responsibility for many roads was shifted from local to regional government, with a consequent decline in local spending on roads. In most other countries, highways account for a not insignificant and generally growing proportion of the local government bill, especially capital expenditure. The causes are easy to see, and are shown in Tables 3.6 and 3.7.

First, the number of private cars is multiplying fast and the average distance travelled by them is also increasing. Second, the number and weight of trucks is increasing, a far more important fact, given what might be called the 'juggernaut effect' whereby wear and tear on the roads increases disproportionately to the weight of the vehicle. A heavy truck or bus does more damage to the roads than a whole fleet of cars. Third, not only is the amount of traffic on existing roads increasing steadily, but the length of public roads is also increasing, and this includes roads which are built and maintained by municipalities. And fourth, as more people switch to private transport, so public transport, which is often a local responsibility, becomes less and less economically viable. The effects on local government costs of these four factors are obvious;

Table 3.6
Increases in motor vehicles in use, 1965-1974

	Percentage increase in passenger cars	*Percentage increase in commercial vehicles*
Denmark	69	—7
Italy	162	133
Norway	91	16
Sweden	47	21
UK	53	7
West Germany	88	27

Source: United Nations, *Statistical Yearbook 1975,* United Nations, 1976, p. 495.
Note: Although the UN Report does not point it out, the fall in commercial vehicles in Denmark is more apparent than real, and is caused by changes in registration and taxation practices.

Table 3.7
Roads and transport

Denmark (per thousand inhabitants)				
Passenger cars	1967:	183.1	1973:	246.9
Trucks and other commercial vehicles		51.6		42.9
Buses		0.9		1.1
Total vehicles		235.6		290.9
Italy				
Cars per thousand inhabitants	1951:	9	1972:	228
Registered vehicles (thousands)				
Cars	1954:	691	1974:	14,295
Trucks		290		1,100
Trucks of 8 tons or more		2		82
Communal extra-urban roads (thousand kms.)		108		143
Passenger vehicles kms. (millions)	1950:	6,940	1973:	186,713
Freight vehicles kms. (millions)		5,150		23,429
Norway				
Total vehicles and trailers (thousands)	1972:	1,273	1976:	1,620
Average kms. travelled by private cars		12,700	1973:	13,200
Length of local roads, kms.	1967:	15,220	1975:	21,523

Table 3.7 (continued)

Norway (continued)				
Municipal roads as % of national total		23		32
Municipal hard surface roads as % of national total		27		35
Sweden				
Buses and lorries (thousands)	1950:	93	1975:	171
Passenger cars in use (thousands)		252	1976:	2,881
Passenger cars per thousand pop.		36		350
Lorries (thousands)		42		165
5 ton lorries (thousands)		1	1977:	36
Total motor vehicles in use		708		3,623
Lorry transportation thousand ton-km.	1972:	14.0	1976:	16.3
Km. roads	1950:	90,409	1975:	97,412
UK				
Local government expenditure on roads, car parks, public transport (£m)	1969/70:	665	1977/8:	910
Local transport subsidies (£m)		2		81
Local authority roads (thousand miles)	1950:	176	1974:	184
Licensed vehicles (millions)	1963:	11.4	1973:	17.0
Licensed goods vehicles of more than 3 tons (thousands)		322		420
Local authority public transport:				
Vehicle miles (millions)		319		280
Passenger journeys (millions)		2.9		2.1
Receipts (£m)		54.7		96.1
Distance travelled by all vehicles (thousand kms.)	1964:	152	1974:	237
West Germany				
Registered vehicles per thousand:				
Cars	1954:	28	1972:	260
Trucks		12		17
Roads maintained by local government, thousand km.	1955:	225	1970:	276
Passenger-kilometres travelled in private cars (millions)		72,500	1972:	444,400
Number of vehicles per km. public road		4.9	1970:	31.6

more money is being invested in the upkeep of old roads and the laying down of new ones; more local effort is going into keeping urban traffic flowing; greater efforts are being devoted to planning and reorganizing traffic systems, marking out bus lanes and parking places, creating pedestrian precincts, devising one-way systems, and policing the highways; and more money is spent on subsidies for public transport.

The last is quite a considerable burden on local finances in some places, most of all in Italy where municipal enterprises run local public transport with traditionally low fares, and with ever increasing losses. The deficit of the public transport agency in Milan was 140 billion lire in 1976, or about 16% of the entire current income of the city government. In Italy as a whole in 1976 the municipal enterprises concerned with local public transport had an estimated deficit of 1,000 billion lire. Losses of this huge magnitude are no doubt special to Italy, but many cities in other countries are currently grappling with public transport losses which add to their total expenses. In Britain, local authority receipts from passenger or transport services almost doubled, 1963-73, but subsidies more than quadrupled, 1969/70-1977/78. Swedish and Norwegian municipalities also subsidize local public transport to a large extent, although not as heavily as in Italy.

Political factors in the demand for increased services

The preceding discussion is enough to show that the demands upon local public services have increased enormously in the post-war era, and that a good deal of this is attributable to demographic changes and increased affluence. But local and central government appear to have played their own part in helping to raise expectations, and it is to these political considerations that the analysis will now turn. The relationship between popular demand and public services is enormously complex, with influence and pressure of varying strengths being generated in many different institutions and channelled to a variety of different official and semi-official bodies, but two aspects of the process seem to be particularly important; the relationship between local government and the general population, and the three-sided relationship between local government, central government, and the general population.

The revolution of rising expectations which has had no less of an impact upon the public sector than the private sector, may well have greater force at the local level of government than at higher levels. This is because local government seems to be closer to the general public, which is more likely to turn to and put pressure upon their local authority than higher and more remote levels of government. In addition, local government, being the grass roots level of democracy, may also respond more readily to citizen demands. These are tentative suggestions, but there is some evidence to support them.

A wide survey of attitudes towards government and politics in five Western nations shows that citizens in all five feel more competent to influence local than central government. The study concludes that 'the sense of subjective competence occurs more frequently vis-à-vis the local government than the national government. This confirms widely held views of the closer relatedness of citizens to their local governments because of their greater immediacy, accessibility, and familiarity'.[2] Fortunately, the survey includes three of the countries covered in this study — Italy, the UK and West Germany — and the figures reproduced in Table 3.8 show that in each case their citizens feel that they are more likely to be effective in attempts to influence local than central government. The differences are considerable in the cases of West Germany and Italy, but more marginal in the UK. Moreover, as Table 3.9 shows, those who feel more competent are more likely to have actually taken action in the past. In other words, citizens do feel that local government is more amenable to their interests and feelings of this kind seem to result in citizen action at the local level.

Public attitudes in Denmark seem to be even more favourable towards local government. At least, when a sample of Danes were asked who they would prefer to take charge of physical planning, a very large majority indeed had a strong preference for local government doing so — more than a third strongly preferred decentralized control compared with barely 2% who strongly preferred the centralization of the service (see Figure 3.1).

Central government also plays an important part in increasing the amount of local activity and spending. Apart from steadily increasing the amount paid in grants to local authorities, it has also

Table 3.8
Attitudes towards local and central government regulations

Percentages who say they can do something about an unjust local or national regulation

	Can do something about local regulation	*Can do something about national regulation*	*(n)*
United States	77	75	(970)
Great Britain	78	62	(963)
West Germany	62	38	(955)
Italy	51	28	(995)
Mexico	52	38	(1,007)

Table 3.9
Attempts to influence local government

Percentage who say they have attempted to influence local government

	Local competents		*Local noncompetents*	
	%	(n)*	%	(n)*
United States	33	(745)	10	(225)
Great Britain	18	(748)	3	(215)
West Germany	21	(590)	2	(365)
Italy	13	(508)	4	(487)
Mexico	9	(531)	2	(476)

* Numbers in parentheses refer to the bases on which percentages are calculated.

Source: Gabriel A. Almond and S. Verba, *The Civic Culture,* Boston: Little, Brown, 1965, pp. 142, 144.

Figure 3.1
Attitudes towards the centralization or decentralization of physical planning in Denmark

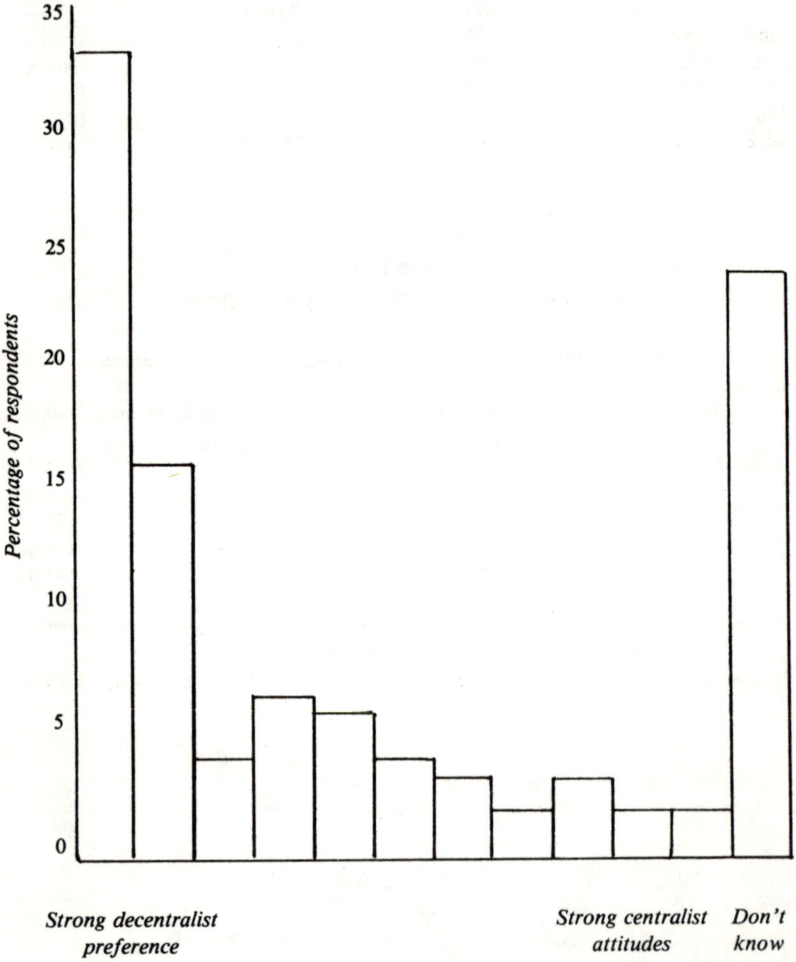

Source: Ole Norgaard Madsen and Soren Winter, 'Borger og Amtskommune', *Danmarks Amstrad*, No. 8, 1975.

encouraged local authorities to provide more and more services for an ever widening range of the public. It does so in many different ways: by increasing the school leaving age, for example; by requiring closer local supervision of planning laws; by asking local authorities to determine and respond to the level of need for special services; and by channelling popular demand back down to the localities and requesting or obliging local authorities to respond to pressure for increased services. In this way, the central government plays a part in regulating the relationship between local government and the public, and also adds a dynamic element to the local system by obliging it or encouraging it to expand.

Democracy thus has its own costs in more ways than one. The more the public participates in local affairs, the higher the costs of local government — officials have to be paid, letters written, phone calls answered, information produced, minutes circulated, delegations received, public hearings held, and demonstrations, peaceful or otherwise, policed. Quite possibly these costs are relatively minor, and few would deny their value, but they also mount up year by year. More important financially, the higher the level of public participation, the higher the level of public demand is likely to be, and the greater the pressure upon government to respond to this demand. The more government does, the greater the range of services it provides, and the more public money it spends, the more people are likely to participate in trying to influence government and its decisions. Hence there is likely to be a spiralling escalation involving participation and public services. In some cases participation hinders government projects — nuclear reactors are not built, road plans cancelled, or urban demolition delayed — but more usually the effect is in the opposite direction.

Summary and conclusions

Local government in most Western European nations is charged with responsibility for a range of services the demand for which has risen steeply in the post-war era. In part this is due to demographic changes, such as the steady increase in the number and proportion of old people in the population, many of whom require local health and welfare services. In part it is due to changing social and economic patterns. Of particular importance here is the fact that working mothers are increasing in numbers, and hence the demand for public pre-school and day-care facilities has expanded rapidly. And in part it is due to a doubling, tripling, or quadrupling of public demand for education at almost every level of the system. Education is usually an expensive public service, and in many countries the costs fall heavily upon local government, especially the expense of primary and secondary schooling which consume by far and away the largest part of the education budget.

Part of the increase is due to the greatly improved social and political sensitivity to the needs of the poor, deviants, and special and minority groups. In many cases the extra responsibility for these groups falls upon local authorities and, consequently, local welfare and education costs have increased rapidly for such groups as drug addicts, alcoholics, the physically and mentally handicapped, immigrants, juvenile delinquents, single parent families, and so on.

And lastly, part of the increase is due to political factors. It seems that local government engenders a greater sense of civic competence among ordinary citizens than higher levels of government, and hence citizens are more likely to act in order to influence local affairs. Survey findings support the idea that people often find local government more accessible and amenable than other levels of government. Consequently, the revolution of rising expectations is likely to have a strong impact on local government which, in turn, is more likely to respond to popular demand. Central government has also contributed to increased service demand and expenditure, for, apart from increasing its grants to local authorities, it has also encouraged and required local government to deliver more services to an ever increasing number of people.

In many ways the steady increase in public demand for local services is a consequence of the great boom in private consumption of the 1950s and 1960s. Although many critics of high levels of public consumption seem to assume that it is incompatible with high levels of private consumption, in reality the two go hand in hand. For example, the huge increase in the number of road vehicles of all kinds has caused the cost of local authority road building and maintenance to mount up steadily over the years. Similarly, increasing affluence combined with the technological demands of the private sector have resulted in more children staying on at school and going on to further and higher education. In these, as in so many other cases, high levels of public and private spending complement and reinforce each other. It is ironic that some of those who call the most loudly for cuts in public spending are precisely the people who, unknowingly perhaps, contribute the most to its upward climb.

The increased demand for local authority services appears to go a long way towards explaining their ever rising cost curves, but the exact pattern varies from one country to another. Danish municipalities, for example, are no longer financially responsible for many roads or for secondary education, and they receive 100% refunds from central government for the pensions they pay. However, they do provide the money for health, social welfare, and day-care services which are becoming increasingly expensive. Swedish municipalities have avoided some of the biggest increases in educational costs by reorganizing the local government system around units which optimize the economic efficiency of schools. German municipalities do not pay teachers' salaries and they share many other education costs with the Länder, but they have borne the costs of heavy capital expenditure for school buildings in the 1950s and 1960s. The education boom has had the biggest impact on the UK where local authorities carry more than 85% of the total national education bill. In sum, the exact incidence of public sector costs between local and other levels of government varies from one country to another, and from one service to another, but in almost every nation, local authorities are charged with the main responsibility for at least one major service, the need or demand for which has mounted steadily over the past two or three decades.

With the exception of secondary education and roads, there is little reason to believe that the overall level of demand for local services will decline in the near future. On the contrary, if more mothers go to work, or if the population grows older and the requirements of minority groups and the unemployed increase, so the need and demand for local services such as health and social welfare, and day-care centres, is likely to grow ever larger.

NOTES

1. OECD, *Public Expenditure on Education*, Paris: OECD 1976.
2. G. A. Almond and S. Verba, *The Civic Culture,* Boston: Little, Brown, 1965, p. 141.

4

New and Improved Services

Introduction

Although it is virtually impossible to define and measure service quality in the public sector, it is clear that local authorities in most countries have increased their spending in the search for improved services. There is ample evidence in each of the six countries to show improvements in education, housing, social welfare, roads, libraries, sports, recreational, and cultural facilities, and many others. Similarly, although local authorities have lost some of their responsibilities to higher levels of government, there are also clear indications that local spending has risen partly because new local services have been introduced, especially in the fields of special education, social welfare, consumer protection, and environmental control. Pressures for new and improved services derive mainly from four quarters: the general public which uses the services; local officials who produce the services; local government, which responds to public pressure, helps to create this pressure, and acts as a pressure group on central government; and central government itself which has encouraged local spending in many different ways.

Quantity and quality

This chapter overlaps and merges with the previous one because there is no clear line of division between service quantity and quality. Indeed, public service quality is often measured in terms of such quantities as pupil-teacher ratios, social worker case loads, and library book stocks, partly because it is relatively easy to do so, but also because it is often difficult to know what other available measures might be used. In fact, many services are brought within the public sector precisely because there is no market test of quality, as there is for many of the products of the private sector. This is not simply a matter of how to measure quality, for there is also the more fundamental issue of how to recognize and define service quality in the first place. Educationalists and social workers have argued about these issues for a very long time, but have reached no conclusion. In the final analysis, perhaps, any evaluation of service quality depends upon political preferences.

The point of this chapter, however, is not to split theoretical and methodological hairs about how to define and measure the quality of public services; even if the quality of some services has not improved in any way whatsoever, the fact remains that local authorities have most usually pursued policies which they *believed* would provide better services, and this has generally added to costs. Improved services do not necessarily mean higher costs, of course. On occasion they may cut costs, but as we shall see in a later chapter, this is not generally the case for public services, especially local public services.

The improved quality of education

Lacking a better measure, and accepting the general view that teaching children is best done by close personal contact, most people have come to accept pupil-teacher ratios as a rough and ready indicator of educational quality. And since the total number of pupils has increased steadily in most countries over the past quarter century, the only way to improve pupil-teacher ratios has been to employ more teachers. The figures in Table 4.1 show that this has happened in all six countries. With two exceptions, the pupil-teacher ratio is better now than at any time in the past thirty years, the exceptions being Norway's secondary school pupil-teacher ratio and Sweden's primary pupils per class which have increased mainly because many small, rural schools have been closed down. In all other cases for which figures are available, the number of teachers

Table 4.1
Indicators of the improved quality of education

Denmark	Up to		Since	
Compulsory education	1973:	7 years	1973:	9 years
Children in non-compulsory kindergarten classes as a % of children in first classes	1967:	7	1977:	69
Pupils with more than nine years at school as a % of pupils in ninth class	1965:	36	1974:	73
Pupils passing upper secondary education (12 years altogether) as a % of 19-year-old population	1965:	10	1975:	18
Number of pupils per class in first to seventh school year	1965:	22	1974:	20
Number of children in retarded classes	1971:	9	1974:	8
Indexed improvement in number of teachers per pupil in primary education	1967:	100	1977:	140
Italy				
Primary pupils per room	1950/1:	34.3	1970/1:	24.6
Primary pupils per class		20.3		17.2
Primary pupils per teacher		27.5		21.8
Primary pupils in special classes (thousands)		57.1		131.3
Percentage primary pupils failing		17.0		7.2
Norway				
Secondary pupils per teacher	1948/9:	13.0	1975/6:	16.7
Primary pupils per teacher		26.1		20.0
Vocational school pupils per teacher		14.8		12.6
Handicapped pupils per teacher	1957:	8.4	1976:	3.0
Volumes in primary school libraries (millions)	1956:	1.5	1975:	4.6
Sweden				
Pupils per special handicapped class	1971:	9.7	1976:	8.8
Primary pupils per class	1950:	21.2	1975:	22.2
Primary pupils per teacher		21.0		19.8
School library books, mills.	1964:	14.0	1974:	25.6

Table 4.1 (continued)

UK (England and Wales)				
Primary pupils per teacher	1950:	28.7	1974:	24.9
Secondary pupils per teacher		21.6		17.5
Number of places in new school buildings, thousands	1966:	268		404
Pupils aged 18 and over as % of population	1964:	3.4		5.4
Graduate primary and secondary teachers as % of all primary and secondary teachers	1971:	22.7	1973:	24.1
New full-time university students, thousands	1949/50:	24.3	1972/3:	67.1
% of school leavers with no 'O' level exam passes	1963/4:	67	1972/3:	39
West Germany				
Primary school pupils per class	1950:	44	1970:	34
Middle school pupils per class		38		32
Secondary school pupils per class		31		28
Special school pupils per class		27		17
New schools:				
Usable area, thousand sq.m.	1965:	2.2	1975:	2.8
Construction costs, per sq.m. usable area, DM		643		1,268
Construction costs index per school building		100		440
General construction cost index		100		180

has outpaced the number of pupils, which means that their ranks have often doubled, trebled, or quadrupled in the past twenty years. Not only this, but the qualifications and training of teachers themselves seem to have improved, or at any rate, the length of training they are required to complete has increased in many countries.

Other evidence about educational quality is scattered and unsystematic, but most indicators in most countries point in the same direction — more and more money has been spent in search of better and better schools and equipment in order to produce better and better qualified pupils. There is evidence of a large school building programme in the 1950s and 1960s in most countries which produced tens of thousands of new school places, built to higher standards, with larger classrooms to house smaller classes. In Germany, for example, new school building increased in size, but spending on school construction rose significantly faster than general building costs, mainly because schools were better equipped with laboratories, language laboratories, and sports halls. Many of the extra amenities were required by State regulations. Schools in other countries are better equipped with furniture, facilities, libraries, and teaching aids, and they are now turning out better qualified pupils than ever before. Illiteracy rates have fallen and examination results have improved. These better trained pupils now proceed to still higher education levels, and in doing so, of course, they swell the size of the education bill still further. In addition, handicapped pupils are increasingly being placed in their own special schools or in classes which are also improving their pupil-teacher ratios.

A more precise estimate of the contribution of improved education quality to increased education costs is contained in a recent OECD publication on *Public Expenditure on Education.*[1] The report is worth summarizing briefly because it supports the conclusions of the last chapter about educational costs, and adds weight to the suggestions of this chapter as well. In discussing the factors which have caused education costs to rise more rapidly than GDP in twenty-one OECD countries between 1963 and the early 1970s, the report examines the impact of three main considerations: demographic changes in the proportion of the school and student aged population; enrolment changes, by which is meant the proportion of the school and student aged population which is actually receiving education; and changes in the cost of education, which is further subdivided into increases in relative prices, and in increases in 'real-inputs', or actual increases in expenditure, after the other factors have been taken into account. In the case of primary and secondary education, demographic changes have had little effect in most countries. Enrolment changes are more important, accounting for about 40% of the increases, slightly more in West Germany and the UK. Cost changes are the most important, accounting for 70% of the increased share of GDP, of which a small proportion (only 6%) can be attributed to an increase in real expenditure. Norway and Sweden, in particular, have increased their real expenditure.

The OECD report suggests that the bulk of the real increase in all countries is probably attributable to increases in teaching and support staff, but it should also be pointed out that the report most probably underestimates the importance of real increases in expenditure. This is because it defines them as the residual which is left over after the other three factors have explained as much as they conceivably can. It also seems to assume that increases in the total educational salary bill are due to increases in salary rates, and not to increases in the number of teachers or to improvements in their qualifications which might also increase their salaries. To this extent, it seems likely that improved service quality has increased education costs, and that this effect is larger than the OECD report suggests.

Improved quality of housing, health and social services

Housing standards have improved markedly in the post-war period. In most countries for which we have evidence, the number of rooms per dwelling has increased, as has the floorspace, the number of houses with basic amenities (such as sewerage, piped water, fixed bath or shower), and the percentage with central heating. The number of persons per dwelling and the number of dwellings per acre has also fallen in most countries. Public and local authority housing has contributed its due share to these rising standards and consequently, the costs of public housing have increased proportionately. One local report on Britain argues that part of the rising costs of municipal housing 'must be attributed to improved standards of equipment and finish, if not space'.[2] However, the report concludes that 'rising standards have been only a minor contributor towards rising costs', and that the most important factor in recent years has been due to a sudden upswing in land values.

Besides building new public housing, local government in some countries plays an important role in planning and making the most of existing housing stocks; in some places, individual houses are modernized by adding rooms and garages, and by connecting them to public sewerage and to water supplies: in other places, whole areas are improved with lawns, trees, playgrounds and other amenities; and in still other areas, slum housing is demolished and replaced. In Italy, for example, 46% of the population was not connected to the public sewerage system in 1951. By 1961 this had

Table 4.2
Indicators of quality for health, housing and social services

Denmark				
Planned staff to resident ratio in old people's homes	1975:	0.70	1980:	0.73
Average size of new dwellings (sq. metres)	1950:	81	1970:	111
Local government's percentage of public sector social and health workers	1972:	77.4	1977:	84.9
Local government's percentage of public sector hospital workers		82.5		91.7
Health and social services as a percentage of total local current expenditure	1966/7:	54.0	1976/7:	61.4
Personnel per person in old people's homes	1975:	0.70	1980:	0.73 (estimate)
Italy				
% population without sewerage	1951:	46	1961:	29
Norway				
Day care services, working expenses (million Kr.)	1967:	27.4	1973:	155
Average economic assistance to people in social care (Kr., current prices)	1969:	791	1974:	1,106
Home helps per pop. aged 70 or over		47.0		27.9
Sweden				
Home help assistance given to handicapped (thousand hours)	1965:	324	1975:	949
UK (England and Wales)				
Pupil teacher ratio in special schools for handicapped and sick	1958:	1 to 1.2	1971:	1 to 1.0
Case loads of probation and after-care workers	1952:	60.2	1973:	31.3
Local authority housing densities (person per acre)	1964:	71.7	1976:	61.7
Slum clearance: housing demolished or closed	1955:	24.4	1976:	48.2

Table 4.2 (continued)

UK (England and Wales) (continued)				
Number of local authority dwellings with renovation grants approved	1964:	32,368	1974:	77,333
Planning applications processed (thousands)	1968:	426	1973:	623
West Germany				
Doctors per thousand population	1952:	13.6	1970:	16.1
Percentage of population with:				
Piped drinking water	1957:	90	1969:	94
Public sewerage		62		79

fallen to 29%. This is not the best indicator of housing quality but it is the only one to hand for Italy, and if more evidence is needed then we can turn to England and Wales where increasingly large numbers of local authority applications for renovation grants have been approved, the number almost doubling from 122,000 in 1964 to 232,000 in 1974. In the same period well over 3 million local authority renovation grants were approved, and 675,000 new houses and flats were built to replace the 700,000 which were demolished or condemned.

Local authority services in health and social welfare have also improved, although indicators are usually difficult to find since there are no simple measures such as pupil-teacher ratios, or housing densities. Nevertheless, scattered evidence suggests the same general trend in the six nations. In Sweden, for example, the number of local authority home help hours devoted to handicapped people has almost trebled in the space of ten years. In Britain, the case loads of probation and after-care workers has virtually halved in twenty years, while the pupil-teacher ratio in special schools has also improved, though not dramatically. In most countries the cost of day-care facilities has also risen, partly because of the big expansion, but also because high standards have been laid down. In Norway, for example, the municipal day-care bill has multiplied five and a half times in only ten years.

Denmark's Social Assistance Act of 1974 expressed a clear concern about improved services for the young, old, and disabled, and the training programme which resulted caused the numbers employed in the social and health sector to rise from 83,600 in 1972 to 108,500 in 1977. Local government's share of this workforce rose from 77.4% to 84.9% in the same period. A good proportion of this increase is due to local government acquiring new responsibilities, but a proportion is also due to rising standards of care. In fact, many improvements in Denmark and elsewhere have been brought about by employing more and better qualified staff, thus increasing the wages and salaries bill — one of the most important items of local expenditure. We shall return to this in a later chapter.

Miscellaneous indicators of service quality

Local government plays an invaluable role in improving the quality of life in many sectors of society besides education, housing, health, and social welfare: roads are built with better surfaces, improved design and brighter lighting, and improved street furniture; technical improvements have also made fire services more efficient, and more capital intensive; larger and larger volumes of refuse are collected and disposed of; better sports and leisure facilities are built; and more and more money is being spent on local authority subsidies to the arts and cultural activities.

This is only a fraction of the story, and it would be impossible and unnecessary to tell it in greater detail. Yet such is the extent to which some public services are taken for granted, especially some local services, that a last and brief illustrative sample of improvements in quality may be useful. Books are readily counted, accurate records easily kept, and library statistics are plentiful. They show large increases in the number of books stocked and borrowed, and in the amount spent on library services by local authorities.

Norway:	Library stocks increased 160% between 1958 and 1977, and loans increased 120% between 1958 and 1975. Three hundred new local libraries were added to the national total.
Sweden:	Library stocks and loans increased almost five times in the quarter of a century leading up to 1976. Library expenditure increased nearly twenty

times in the same period.

UK: In England and Wales local public library stocks nearly doubled and library staff increased 40% in only nine years between 1963 and 1972. Professionally trained staff increased in numbers. Current and capital expenditure on libraries, museums and art galleries rose by an average amount for local services during this period, but this was, of course, a larger increase than that for all public services.

Sources of demand for improved service quality

Enough evidence has been produced to show that services now cost more than ever partly because local authorities have spent more in search of improved standards, but where has this pressure for quality come from? There seems to be four main sources — the consumers of services, the producers of services, local representatives, and central government.

The first source is the most obvious one and it is generated by the demands and standards of those who use public services. In spite of that army of pessimists and cynics who believe that nothing is as good as it used to be, standards for many kinds of goods and services, whether publicly or privately produced, have risen steadily over the past twenty-five years. The economic boom of the 1950s and 1960s put real buying power behind this trend, and the ramifications were felt no less strongly in local government than elsewhere. Perhaps they were even more strongly felt. For the past decade, citizens in most communities in Western Europe have pushed and pressured, demanded and demonstrated for ever improved services, just as they have steadily resisted any attempts to erode standards. This is most evident in the recent surge of activity on the part of the local groups, voluntary organizations, and associations, The list of such organizations could be very long but, in the main, it consists of community groups, tenants' associations, residents' associations, environmental groups, parent-teacher associations, minority group organizations, taxpayers' associations, militant social welfare lobbies, housing pressure groups, amenity societies, groups formed to oppose the construc-

Table 4.3
Miscellaneous indicators of improved service quality

Denmark				
Public library books (millions)	1967:	14.5	1977:	37.6
Public library loans (millions)		34.2		95.4
Norway				
Municipal hard surfaced roads as % of all local roads	1967:	17.2	1975:	27.2
Number of public libraries	1957:	1,078		1,402
Library books issued (millions)	1958:	6.9		15.1
Public library book stock (millions)		4.1	1977:	10.6
Sweden				
County and municipal library book stocks (millions)	1950:	6.8	1976:	32.1
Book loans (millions)		15.2		73.5
Library expenditure (million Cr.)		4.5		87.0
Municipal grants to local theatres (thousand Cr.)	1968/9:	13.7	1975/6:	69.0
Municipal grants to local orchestras (thousand Cr.)		8.8		20.4
UK (England and Wales)				
Ratio of policemen to population	1949:	1 to 700	1971:	1 to 500
Ratio to firemen to population	1951:	1 to 2,500		1 to 2,100
Local authority air pollution monitoring sites	1949:	526	1974:	2,045
Local authority revenue expenditure on libraries, museums, and art galleries (£m)	1951/2:	10	1972/3:	90
Local authority revenue expenditure on parks and open spaces (£m)		16		108
Local authority total expenditure on swimming pools (£m)		1.1		60.0
Public library book stocks (million)	1963	56	1972:	101
Public library staff (thousands)		17		24

tion of urban expressways, the fluoridation of water supplies, and changes in the educational system, and spontaneous protest and action groups of all kinds.

Some local groups are not new, of course, for most communities have had a variety of politically active organizations in them for many years, including business and professional associations, and trade unions. Trade unions are particularly important in Italy, where, as part of movement out of the factory and into the community, they have applied themselves to the task of improving local services. This interest in community affairs characterized many Western societies in the 1960s and 1970s and many of the groups involved have increasingly used militant and aggressive tactics which give them more visibility and perhaps more power as well.

Much of the evidence for the growth of community organizations is impressionistic, but it is borne out by observers in a variety of different countries, and, in addition, we are fortunate to have one study which compared the state of affairs in 1950 with that in 1967. The report concludes:

> One of the most striking changes in the map of voluntary associations in 1967 compared with 1950 was the rise of local pressure groups. . . there has been a multiplication of specialist pressure groups, such as tenants associations, conservationist associations, associations for those specifically handicapped in some way. These would seem to be the response of people to the increased scale and complexity of the decision-making process on the one hand and of increased geographic mobility of sections of the population on the other.[3]

The report then goes on to document the ways in which a variety of newly established groups, plus a few of the older organizations, have pressurized the local council on education, snow-clearing, local taxes, public housing, the state of pavements, historical preservations, rural amenities, and urban development.

Behind many of the new community groups, as the quotation above suggests, is the increased mobility of the population. In both Norway and Sweden the annual population movement across local authority boundaries has increased, while in the UK about 10% of the population moves house each year, and about 33% move every five years. The figure in the UK is increasing. A good deal of this movement involves middle class people leaving the city for the surrounding suburbs, towns and villages. In Germany, for example, the post-war trend has been for well trained and qualified people to move to major urban agglomerations around Munich, Stuttgart, Frankfurt, and Cologne, a great number of them settling not in the central cities but in satellite towns and villages. In Germany, as in other places, this relocation of the population entails the movement of a cosmopolitan middle class carrying its high urban standards for public services into small towns and rural communities which often have poorer public services. Once established these social groups tend to form their own local organizations which become active in local politics, and press for better local services. At the same time, the suburban and newly rural middle class is likely to use some city services and demand a high standard of provision there too — libraries, museums, theatres, athletic tracks, swimming pools, parks, and so on. The residents of the suburbs surrounding Oslo are among the groups which press strongly for high quality services in that city.

The second set of pressures for better local services has come not from those who consume services but from those who produce them. As local government has become a bigger business which begins to rival even the larger industries in the private sector, so it has developed its professional staff. This has had three separate effects on local costs. First, these highly trained experts have inevitably added to the salary bill. Second, professional workers have, by virtue of their professional ethic and their sense of service to their clients, been a powerful force for improving service quality, a force, moreover, which has the advantage of operating inside local government, rather than as an outside pressure group. And to some extent, ambitious professionals are bound to want bigger empires for themselves, and to press for more staff and bigger departmental budgets. Third, highly trained professional workers sometimes require expensive equipment, special buildings, and large back-up teams to help them in their work.

Evidence about increasingly large and professionally trained teaching and social worker staffs has already been produced, and can be augmented with the following examples.

Planners: Planning departments have been established or expanded in almost every large Western European city. Professional planners now have their own special training and qualifications, and they also need research and development staffs to help them.

Statisticians:	Many large cities have their own statistical department to service their elected and appointed officials, and some have quite large research and social survey units.
Managers:	Local government has borrowed managerial skills from the private sector, and has developed some of its own. As it becomes larger so it builds up specialist, managerial skills and buys equipment, such as computers, to go with them.
Schools:	Education administration has developed its own training and its own career structure. In addition, modern schools often require language laboratories, video recorders, televisions, physical education facilities, desk calculators, and so on.
Police (UK only):	Police forces are recruiting more university graduates and equipping themselves with forensic laboratories, radios, computers, as well as developing special units for drugs, vice, fraud, and weaponry.
Social services:	To the growing ranks of social workers have been added a range of specialists who cater for the needs of the old and the handicapped, the mentally ill and handicapped, and the disabled. They also require special equipment in the form of transport for the aged and the handicapped, specially built and equipped schools for the physically and mentally handicapped, community centres, playgrounds, residential homes, and a variety of facilities for the blind and the deaf. The latest traffic lights, for example, have audio signals for the blind, and pedestrian under-passes and bridges (themselves relatively new) are now built with ramps for wheelchairs.
Finance officers:	City finances have long been staffed by highly trained experts, but they are increasingly beginning to acquire forward planning departments, professional economists, and increasing quantities of computer hardware and software. And they will now have to find extra money to buy books on the financial problems of local government in Western Europe.

Housing: Housing management is itself beginning to become a specialist activity, besides which housing departments seem to be pressing for more spacious and better looking housing developments. There is some evidence that local authority architects in the UK were not unimportant in pressing for high rise developments which turned out to be more expensive than conventional houses.

Local councils seem to have contributed something to the pressure for improved services, not just by employing specialists and buying new equipment, but also by responding to citizen demands, and perhaps even by going out of their way to seek these demands. We have already seen in a previous chapter how the general public feels better able to influence local government than other levels of government, and how this feeling seems to be translated into actual activity. It is possible, therefore, that local government is subject to considerable public pressure, both of a routine nature and of a more militant pressure group kind. The close connection between municipal authorities and citizens can be illustrated with an example: the Housing Department of the city of Birmingham in England reports that it deals with 200,000 inquiries from the public in a year. This is probably not unusual for a large department in a city of a million people, for local government often appears to be making a genuine effort to bridge the gap between itself and its citizens by opening up information centres, appointing public relations officers, and keeping the general public informed of its activities by way of public exhibitions. Even if some of this is no more than political window dressing, and even if some of it is well intentioned but ineffective, this still leaves room for the argument that local government is more responsive to citizen demands than other levels of government. To this extent, its sensitivity to citizen demands may have led it to search for the high quality services which the general public seems to expect, and to make efforts to tell the public about these services.

Examples of local government reaching out to the general public include the fact that some German cities open their local government offices in the evening so that they can be visited out of normal working hours. In addition, small, community offices have been opened on the periphery of some of the larger cities, thus making it unnecessary to travel to the city centre. In Denmark, the city of Aarhus has recently opened a 'city plan shop' to inform residents of local plans. The example is being followed by other Danish cities. In Italy, the city of Bologna has developed a computer network which enables local offices to communicate rapidly and accurately with their headquarters, thus making it unnecessary for officials and members of the public to travel to the city centre. In Britain, some cities are running a 'planning bus' which tours the neighbourhoods so that people can see what is planned for their area, and register their opinion about it in the appropriate place. Outlying rural areas are also acquiring their own library buses which tour small villages, and increasingly the small libraries are circulating their stocks in order to give the public a wider choice of books.

Besides having its own pressure groups, local government also acts as a pressure group itself. It is constantly putting pressure of one kind or another on central government in its search for more and better services, constantly pressing for more central government money, and constantly using its official weight and status as a democratically elected tier of government in order to make central government facilitate its policy aspirations.

Central government also plays its role, laying down minimum standards for vital services such as education, housing, social services and public health, and by making recommendations and guidelines for other services. The federal law of 1972/3 on social aid and youth welfare is an example in West Germany, and Norway, Denmark, Sweden and the UK all have an elaborate array of central regulations governing the performance of local authorities. West Germany has some formal national standards and the Länder prescribe such things as pupil-teacher ratios, class sizes, building regulations for schools and hospitals, and so on. In Italy, national standards do not exist for any area other than building regulations. An Act of 1967 laid down a range of regulations for building, densities, and the mix of residential and industrial developments, and although it is still too early to measure the effect, it seems to have had some impact in setting minimum standards. An Act of 1974 in Denmark dealt with levels of provision for the young, the old and the handicapped, all of whom are partially the responsibility of the municipalities.

In general, the number and variety of national minimum standards, guidelines, and recommendations is increasing. Their impact on local spending is difficult to estimate even roughly, but it is probable that their overall effect is to raise spending, mainly because some authorities with low standards are likely to try to raise them, in order to meet national guidelines, while those with high standards are unlikely to lower them. One social welfare official in Germany is reported as saying: 'Thank God for national standards. Without them I would have had to cut my budget'. And a study of budgeting in Oslo suggests that state regulations play a part, albeit a small one, in determining the success of budgeting proposals.[4] In the opinion of a British report: 'At least in the years since the First World War the impetus for most of the expenditure is to be found in legislation. The overwhelming proportion of legislation that required, encouraged or permitted local authority spending was public general legislation... Ministers and departments have had many opportunities to halt the succession of Bills, regulations or circulars that would be likely to create further expenditure'.[5] British local authorities also recognize the role played by central government in pressing for higher and higher standards: '... some government departments urged local authorities to develop and expand their services. Legislation was promoted, circulars were published and loan sanctions were granted, all designed to encourage expansion or improvement'.[6]

The 'levelling-up' process

The combined effects of central and local government action, and of citizen pressures for better services can be seen in the levelling-up or equalization process which has characterized many local government systems in Western Europe since 1945. Central government has put pressure on local government in general, and on the poorer and more backward authorities in particular, to improve standards, and although it has usually made money available to do so, local authorities have often felt that the amounts were inadequate. Local authorities have not only responded to central pressure, but some of them may have helped to create it themselves by setting high standards, by competing with each other, and by pressing central government to encourage or require local authorities to provide

Table 4.4
Per capita expenditure in Norwegian communes (N.Kr., constant prices, 1966 = 100)

	Rural	Index	Urban	Index	Ratio, Urban/Rural
Capital expenditure					
1950	228.5	100	494.7	100	2.2
1971	634.1	277	909.1	184	1.4
Current expenditure					
1950	323.2	100	999.8	100	3.1
1971	1,179.5	365	1,892.7	189	1.6

Table 4.5
Percentage annual growth rates in total expenditure, Swedish municipalities

	Cities of 50,000 or more	*Rural municipalities*	*Total local expenditure*
1950-54	13.0	13.1	13.0
1955-59	8.2	9.5	8.6
1960-64	14.1	15.4	14.5
1965-67	16.0	11.3	14.6
1950-67	12.2	11.5	12.0

more and better services. And some local residents have done their bit by demanding more and more of local government, and by contributing to a climate of opinion which favours greater social equality between regions. It is quite probable that political pressure for equality between areas is greater now than at any time in the past.

The trend towards greater equality between areas can be seen clearly in the spending histories of urban and rural communes in Norway in the past twenty-five years. Per capita and current expenditure used to be three times higher in the urban communes, and capital expenditure twice as high. But since 1950 the rural communes have increased their spending so much that a good deal of this gap has closed (see Table 4.4). This trend reflects the Norwegian government's policy of equalization between areas.

Sweden has followed a similar path towards equalization, but only for part of the post-war period. As a result of the amalgamation reforms of 1952, spending in the smaller and isolated municipalities began to rise rather quickly, but after about 1965 the cities began to outstrip the rural areas once again (Table 4.5). The effect was to raise spending levels in the rural areas, although the trend was not sustained, as it was in Norway. These differences are probably due to the divergent policies of the two countries: Norway has favoured a policy of decentralization which has entailed raising the standards of the periphery, while Sweden has been more centralist, and concentrated rather more on the big cities in the last decade.

The West Germans have also tried to iron out regional disparities in public service provision. A recent report (Raumordnungsbericht) has documented rather greater inequalities than were generally assumed, mainly between the urban and rural Länder, and between major urban agglomerations, such as the Ruhr Valley and Frankfurt, and small urban centres. Since the mid 1960s, federal laws (Raumordnungsgesetz von 1965) and state development plans have been used in an attempt to reduce these disparities. Their impact is difficult to assess partly because some policies have been in operation for only a short time, and partly because they have been implemented with different degrees of enthusiasm in different areas, but it seems most likely that they have improved service standards and increased expenditure in some places, though not in others.

The cost of new local government services

In the same way that it is difficult to draw any clear line of division between service quality and service quantity, so it is difficult to distinguish between a new service and one which has been greatly expanded and improved. For example, some local authorities have been involved in minor ways with consumer protection and environmental protection for several decades, but the extent of their activities are now so much greater that they are virtually new responsibilities. For this reason much of the argument and evidence about service quantity and service quality also applies to this section about new services. For all practical purposes service quantity, service quality, and service innovations are simply different aspects of the same thing.

Perhaps the main point to be made is that local government in many countries has been acquiring and developing a range of new services which have contributed to its rising cost curves. At the same time, of course, many local government systems have lost responsibility for some services to other public agencies, and this has reduced some of their financial pressures. But whereas the loss of functions is widely recognized (and sadly lamented among defenders of local government), the steady accumulation of new responsibilities is almost as widely overlooked. There are good reasons for this. Responsibility for a few major services has been taken away from local government in some countries, and the termination has often been clear and sharp. In contrast, the accumulation of a large number of smaller responsibilities has often gone unnoticed, mainly because they usually start in a minor way, and grow steadily but unspectacularly over the years. Of course, the initial costs of new services rarely match those of recently lost ones, and, indeed, it is impossible to make any exact calculations about the net financial consequences of such gains and losses, but a brief survey of recent events in the five countries suggests that new service costs are not insubstantial.

Denmark: In the past decade or so Danish municipalities have lost their responsibilities for some major services, including health insurance, secondary schools, and some roads. On the other hand, municipalities have the task of providing day-care facilities for children and accommodation for old people, both rapidly expanding and expensive services. They have also been given major responsibility for pollution control and consumer protection, both of which are growing in importance and expense.

Italy: Local government in Italy has not lost any major functions in recent years, and it has been given an extensive range of new tasks by central government. In fact, one of the worst problems facing Italian communes has been the need to finance these additional responsibilities, without matching funds. According to one comentator: 'The State has continually charged the communes with responsibility for services and public works which are beyond their financial competence. . . In fact, by doing this the State has clearly followed an unfair policy. In charging the communes and other local agencies with responsibility for services which should have been provided by the State, the budget of central administration has been streamlined, but at the expense of the local budgets'.[7]

Norway: Norwegian local government has not lost any major responsibilities in recent years, but it has gained a variety of both minor and major ones as a result of national legislation in the areas of education, social services, planning, health, environmental protection, culture, and the provision of kindergartens.

Sweden: Although Swedish communes have lost some responsibilities (e.g. the police force was centralized in 1965) the whole purpose of the reforms of 1952 and 1962 was to enable them to carry out a wider range of functions with greater efficiency. In this respect the reforms were undoubtedly successful. The development of events has been summarized in the following way: 'The number of duties imposed on communes by the state has greatly increased. . . Simultaneously, however, such communal services as are in no way or only remotely regulated by the state have developed enormously, for example, housing, gas, electricity, water and drainage, transport, roads, as well as various cultural needs such as libraries, theatres, assembly halls, sports and recreation grounds, etc.'.[8]

UK: Like Denmark, some fairly important services have been transferred from local government to other public bodies, including responsibility for the few major roads that remained under local control, health services, public assistance, valuation and rating assessment, civil defence, and water supply. There is little doubt that these changes have reduced local government costs by a substantial amount. On the other hand, local authorities have also acquired the rights and duties to perform a whole range of new tasks, including some whose costs are not inconsiderable. A full list would be extremely long, even for the past decade, but, by way of illustration, it includes: community development, pre-school provision, environmental protection, housing, community homes, probation, services for the chronically sick and disabled, care and after-care for the mentally handicapped, fire inspection, consumer protection, preservation of buildings and trees, parking facilities, family planning advice, structure planning, caravan sites, the education of handicapped children, waste disposal, health and safety standards at work and legal advice centres. The total costs of these services may not entirely off-set the services losses mentioned earlier (although they have certainly done a good deal to fill the vacuum) but it would be wrong to overlook their contribution to the mounting costs of local government in the UK.

West Germany: Police functions were transferred from the cities to the Länder in the 1950s, but the federal government and the Länder gave local government responsibilities for housing, planning, and environmental protection as well as important — and costly — assignments for social welfare and youth work. Social and Youth Welfare Acts in 1972-3 both expanded local responsibilities and set national minimum standards for these services.

Summary

In spite of the insoluble problems of defining and measuring service quality in the public sector, it is clear that most local authorities in most countries have spent increasing amounts of money in an attempt to improve the quality of their services and facilities. In education, not only has the pupil-teacher ratio improved in virtually every case for which we have evidence in our six countries, but the qualifications of the teachers themselves appear to have improved, as have the spaciousness of school buildings, and the quality of equipment and facilities. An OECD survey shows that the bulk of increases in educational expenditure in the early 1970s was attributable to increased student numbers and to the rising costs of education, but a small proportion of the increase was also due to the research for improved educational quality. Another report on housing standards and costs also concludes that improved standards have contributed to rising costs, although, once again, the effect seems to have been more marginal than major. It is not difficult to find other evidence of improvements in social services, roads, libraries, sports and cultural facilities, police and fire services, and in parks and open spaces. These have probably contributed to the rising cost curves of local government, although it is not possible to say by how much they have added to the total bill.

The pressure for better quality services seems to have originated from four main quarters. First, the general public appears to have demanded better public services, and there is evidence of an increasing number and variety of community groups which put pressure upon local government to improve its performance. These groups appear to have been stimulated by the increased geographical mobility of the population, especially the middle class population, which has migrated to small rural towns and to the satellite communities which ring most major urban areas. In doing so they have carried with them their high standards for public services into areas which previously had rather low standards.

Second, the producers of services have also helped raise the quality and therefore the cost of services, partly out of a sense of duty to their clients, partly because of empire-building motives, partly because they sometimes encourage the purchase of expensive capital equipment, and partly because highly trained, professional staff costs money. Third, local government has probably contributed its share towards improved service standards, not only because its grass roots proximity to the general public predisposes it to respond more quickly to citizen demands than other levels of government, but also because there may be a certain amount of competition between authorities to see which can be the most modern and innovative. Local government has also acted as a pressure group which has encouraged central government to increase its grants and introduce legislation laying down minimum standards. Fourth, central government has imposed its own standards upon local government by laying down national guidelines and recommending minimum standards. These have often been accompanied by extra grants, but local authorities often complain that the extra resources are insufficient.

The combined effect of these four sets of pressures on service standards can be seen in the 'levelling-up' or equalization process which seems to have marked most countries in Western Europe since the early 1960s. There is clear evidence that the low spending rural communes of Norway have raised their expenditure year by year with the help of central grants, so closing the gap between themselves and the higher spending urban communes. This has been done very largely in the name of social equality between areas. The same pattern repeated itself in Sweden, at least up until about 1965 when once again the larger cities began outspending the rural areas. A policy of equalization has also been implemented in West Germany, and central govenrment grants in the UK have long been distributed with the intention of bringing the poorer areas up to the standards of the richer areas.

The introduction of an entirely new range of duties is closely connected with both improvements in service quality and increases in sheer quantity; improved quality, increased quantity, and innovation are simply different aspects of the same thing. In all six countries, local government has acquired new tasks over the past twenty or thirty years, and although many of these start off as relatively inexpensive, they have a habit of growing steadily until they become considerable items on the local budget. Most of these additional responsibilities seem to fall within the province of social services, special education, consumer protection, environmental control and planning, pollution control, and health care, although they range over a hundred and one different areas. Denmark and the UK have also lost some major responsibilities to other public agencies, but in Denmark, these losses have been very largely off-set by additional social services and health care responsibilities, while in the UK the acquisition of a large number of small tasks has helped to fill the financial vacuum left by the loss of a few major services. A major problem for Italian communes is the growing number of new responsibilities passed on to them by the central government which, however, has not increased grants in proportion.

NOTES

1. OECD, *Public Expenditure on Education*, Paris: OECD, 1976, pp. 9-30.

2. Valerie A. Kahn, *Housing Standards and Costs*, University of Brimingham, Centre for Urban and Regional Studies, Occasional Paper No. 25, 1973, p. 47.

3. Margaret Stacey, et al., *Power, Persistence and Change*, London: Routledge and Kegan Paul, 1975, pp. 56-7.

4. Tore Hansen, 'Central Controls and Local Budgeting Behaviour: A Test of Some Partial Models', *Policy and Politics*, 6 (March 1978), 299-319.

5. *Report of the Committee of Inquiry into Local Government Finance* (Layfield), Cmnd 6453, London: HMSO, 1976, p. 32.

6. Ibid, p. 10.

7. M. S. Giannini, 'I Communi', *L'Ordinamento comunale e provinciale*, Vicenza: Neri Pozza, 1967, p. 38.

8. Per Langenfelt, *Local Government in Sweden*, Stockholm: The Swedish Institute, 1964, pp. 16-17.

5

The Increased Cost of Services

Introduction

This chapter shows that for reasons which are largely beyond its control, local government is particularly susceptible to increasing price levels and has, therefore, had to carry the extra burden of rising costs during the past decade of inflation. In the first place, local government is labour intensive by comparison with central government, and salaries and wages tend to increase more rapidly than other costs during inflationary periods. In the second place, local government in the UK, West Germany, and Italy has had to borrow relatively large sums of money, and this has generated heavy debt charges. In the third place, many local authorities are heavily involved in construction activities and land purchasing, and the cost of both have increased rather sharply in the recent past. Lastly, the chapter shows that local government is more heavily involved in public consumption expenditure than central government, and this type of spending seems to be particularly sensitive to price increases. In sum, the chapter shows that the costs of local services seem to have risen more rapidly than other costs in the public or private sector, particularly during recent years of high inflation, and this has occurred for reasons which have little or nothing to do with local government, but which are quite beyond its sphere of influence.

Inflation and local government costs

The public sector is often said to suffer from inflation, and to have suffered particularly acutely during the period of double figure inflation which many Western countries experienced during the 1970s. This is because public sector costs tend to rise more rapidly during inflationary periods than other costs. It has also been said that within the public sector, local government suffers most from inflation. As a recent Council of Europe study has put it: 'All European countries are affected to a greater or lesser extent by inflation, and local and regional government, which is an extremely labour-intensive industry and is obliged to provide services with very heavy operating costs, is particularly adversely affected'.[1] If this is the case, it would go a long way towards explaining why local costs have accelerated relatively rapidly over the past decade.

The Swedish government has tried to calculate the differential rate of inflation for central and local government, and for the private sector, and although there are considerable difficulties with this task, the figures are revealing, nonetheless.

Table 5.1
Implicit price indices for local central government and private consumption in Sweden (1960 = 100)

	1960	*1964*	*1968*	*1972*
Local government consumption	100	126	180	245
Central government consumption	100	124	164	197
Private consumption	100	113	134	167
GNP	100	115	138	171

Source: Kommunernas ekomomi 1960-1970, *Betänkande au Kommanal-Ekomomiska utredningen,* SOU 1976:45, Stockholm, 1976.

It is evident that inflation has been substantially higher for local government than for either central government or the private sector in Sweden, and that local government suffered most in the late 1960s and early 1970s. According to the Swedish report, the main reason for this is the relatively high proportion of local spending which goes on wages and salaries.

But what of the other countries? Clearly, a rigorous and systematic measure of the effect of inflation on local government costs would be exceedingly difficult to establish, if only because the information necessary to take account of the complexities of the public sector economics at different levels of government does not exist in one country, never mind a series of them.[2] But it is possible to illustrate, though not actually test, the proposition that local government is more adversely affected by inflation than central government, at least for the rather small number of countries for which we have some evidence. The method is as follows: first, identify a set of countries where local government expenditure has increased at a faster rate than central government expenditure; then, identify the countries with higher than average inflation rates; and finally, see if the countries with relatively high growth rates of local expenditure are also the countries with the high inflation rates. The figures in Table 5.2 suggest that they are. Data are available for only nine countries and this is too small a number from which to draw firm conclusions but, nevertheless, the distribution is what one would expect. Of the four countries with low inflation rates, three also have a relatively low growth of local expenditure, and of the

Table 5.2
Inflation and the growth of local expenditure, 1970-75

		Countries in which the rate of inflation was:	
		Low	High
Countries in which local expenditure has grown:	Slower than central government's	3	1
	Faster than central government's	1	4

Note: The nine countries for which inflation rates and central and local government expenditures are available are Belgium, Finland, France, The Netherlands, Norway, Sweden, UK, and Spain.

Source: National Accounts of OECD Countries, Volume II (Detailed Tables), Paris: OECD, 1975.

five countries with high inflation rates, four have relatively fast rates of growth in local expenditure. In sum, in these nine nations local government expenditure has grown faster than central expenditure in the countries with high inflation rates.

Labour costs

It is possible to identify rather more exactly the effects of inflation on local costs. The first and probably the most popular theory is that local government is labour intensive, and that labour costs tend to climb more rapidly than other costs during inflationary times. The labour intensity of local government has already been suggested in the Swedish and Council of Europe reports quoted above, and in discussions in previous chapters in this report of pupil-teacher ratios and social worker case loads. Many other local departments are also labour intensive, including planning and architecture, fire and police, housing and public health, personal health, and general administration. In all these cases, the task carried out either depends upon personal contact and understanding, or else consists of non-routine tasks which cannot be mechanized. This is not to say that machines cannot help local government, nor that its workers cannot be replaced to a limited extent by machines or capital intensive forms of production, but the degree to which this is possible is obviously limited in many areas of local government activity.

The labour intensive nature of local services is reinforced by the generally held view that service quality can be measured in terms of labour intensity. Thus educational pressure groups often push for better pupil-teacher ratios, and their counterparts in social welfare frequently argue for more social work staff. In other words, the labour intensity of local departments is not only an economic fact of life, it is also treated as a social and political fact of life by groups which struggle for better services.

These considerations help to explain why local services are becoming more labour intensive as time passes. At least the figures presented in Tables 5.3 and 5.4 show that local authorities are employing more people each year. Table 5.3 presents some detailed statistics for a selection of nineteen towns and cities in Denmark, Norway, Sweden, and West Germany. In every case, with the minor exception of Aalborg in Denmark, and the major exception of Stockholm in Sweden, the number of staff paid from the main

Table 5.3
Staff paid from local authority main accounts

Country	*Town*	*1970*	*1972*	*% increase 1970-2*
Denmark	Viborg	1,648	1,811	9.9
	Silkeborg	1,760	1,890	7.4
	Esbjerg	2,652	2,695	1.6
	Aalborg	6,796	6,732	-0.9
	Aarhus	8,714	9,355	7.4
Norway	Bodo	581	678	16.7
	Stavanger	2,280	2,445	7.2
	Trondheim	3,500	3,700	5.7
Sweden	Lidingo	1,068	1,176	10.1
	Umea	3,386	3,819	12.8
	Vasteras	4,070	4,290	5.4
	Goteborg	29,313	33,350	13.8
	Stockholm	66,700	48,500	-27.3
West Germany	Siegen	810	830	2.5
	Hamm	1,522	1,585	4.1
	Munster	2,578	2,823	9.5
	Krefeld	3,791	4,025	6.2
	Dusseldorf	10,908	11,754	7.8
	Munchen	40,357	41,785	3.5
Total number of towns: 19			% increase	5.4

Source: Council of Europe, *Standardized European Local Accounts,* 1970, 1971, 1972, Study Series on Local and Regional Authorities in Europe, Volumes, II, IV, VII, and IX, Strasbourg: 1977. Figures for a selection of Italian towns were not available when this table was compiled.

Note: While it would be unwise to compare figures for different cities and countries, it is perfectly in order to compare the same city at different points in time. In other words, the table should be read across, but not down the columns.

Table 5.4
Local government employees, wages and salaries

Denmark				
Local authority employees as a % of the public sector workforce	1972:	59.8	1977:	63.1
Full-time local government employees (thousands)		244		313

Table 5.4 (continued)

Italy				
Indexed cost of salaries (1960 = 100)				
Total public administration	1960:	100	1972:	153.6
Communes		100		141.2
Consumer price index		100		119.0
Norway				
Local government salaries and wages as a % of local current expenditure				
Urban communes	1966:	69.5	1971:	63.9
Rural communes		66.1		63.7
Local government employees (thousands)	1967:	26.6	1975:	36.1
Indexed increase in municipal wages and salaries (1967 = 100)		100		208
Consumer price index		100		176
Sweden				
Local government employees (including some part-time) (thousands)	1965:	268.4	1975:	490.0
Local government employees as a % of national workforce	1960:	7.0	1972:	17.0
UK				
Local employees as a % of national workforce	1952:	6.2	1975:	11.3
Central government employees as % of national workforce (civilians only)		5.3		6.5
West Germany				
Wages and salaries as a % of total expenditure				
All government	1950:	20.9	1969:	25.3
Federal government		2.3		11.8
Länder		42.0		47.6
Local government		29.8		24.5
Full-time local government employees (thousands)		550	1976:	848

Table 5.5
Salaries and wages as a percentage of central and local government expenditure

	Local government			*Central government*	
	% of current expenditure	*% of total expenditure*		*% of current expenditure*	*% of total expenditure*
Denmark					
1972/3	30.3	26.7		20.7	19.4
1974/5	36.0	31.9		21.6	20.4
Italy					
1950/1	46.3	37.9		38.3	31.9
1972/3	32.7	27.7		27.7	25.0
Norway					
1950/1	41.5	21.4		19.4	12.2
1976/7	62.1	31.0		18.9	12.8
Sweden					
1960/1	45.7	37.9	1961/2	18.5	15.8
1975/6	43.1	35.7	1976/7	15.1	13.7
UK					
1963/4	52.1				
1976/7	48.1	38.5	1972	18.9	16.8
West Germany					
1960/1	45.7	23.7		10.8	8.5
1973/4	44.1	28.7		21.5	17.3

account of local authorities increased from 1970 to 1972. The increases range from almost 2% to over 16%, with an average of 5.4%, or close to 1.8% per annum. Figures in Table 5.4 also show that Danish local government employs a large and increasing proportion of the public sector workforce, and that local authorities in Norway, Sweden, Britain, and West Germany are employing more and more people. Indeed, Swedish municipalities increased their workforce by an annual average of no less than 7.5% for the years 1965-75.

It is also evident that labour costs absorb a larger proportion of local government spending compared with central government. Table 5.5 shows that in each of the six nations, local government spends proportionately more on wages and salaries than central government. Overall the figures show that local government is not just more labour intensive than central government, but considerably more so. To this extent, the labour intensity of local government may help to explain its rapidly mounting costs in inflationary periods.

Nevertheless, a close link between labour intensity and mounting local government costs has never been established with the help of hard facts and figures. When the facts and figures are assembled, the case for labour intensity as a major cause of the local resource squeeze turns out to be rather weak. In the first place, although the local salary bill may well increase, this is not a serious matter for local government in some countries, simply because their central government bears some or all these costs. In Germany, for example, the Länder pay teachers' salaries, and in Italy the communes pay only a small proportion of teachers' salaries.

In the second place, although local government staff has usually increased, and although wages and salaries may have increased faster than prices, in general the fact remains that wages and salaries have *decreased* as a percentage of local expenditure in Italy, Sweden, the UK and West Germany. In other words, although labour costs have risen, they have not risen as fast as total local government expenditure (see Table 5.5).

This conclusion is drawn from an analysis of long term trends in costs, and it might be argued that special attention should be paid to the effects of double figure inflation in recent years. Unfortunately, data for this period are not yet available since it usually takes several years to reach the international source books (if they

Table 5.6
Salaries and wages as a percentage of total current expenditure

Country	*Town*	*1970*	*1972*	*% change*
Denmark	Viborg	25.7	31.5	+5.8
	Silkeborg	20.6	25.7	+5.1
	Esbjerg	24.2	29.0	+4.8
	Aalborg	21.6	26.4	+4.8
	Aarhus	24.6	26.3	+1.7
Norway	Bodo	36.2	38.7	+2.5
	Stavanger	42.0	41.5	—0.5
	Trondheim	39.9	55.2	+15.3
Sweden	Lidingo	51.6	49.1	—2.5
	Umea	67.9	66.9	—0.1
	Vasteras	54.8	54.8	0.0
	Goteborg	56.0	56.8	+0.9
	Stockholm	51.6	44.1	—7.6
West Germany	Siegen	52.2	49.2	—3.0
	Hamm	49.5	48.2	—1.3
	Munster	54.2	52.2	—2.0
	Krefeld	47.4	48.4	+1.0
	Dusseldorf	42.1	44.2	+2.0
	Munchen	55.7	54.8	—0.9
Total number of towns:19				Average change +1.3

Source: See Table 5.3

Note: As with Table 5.3, this table should be read across and not down. In other words, it is possible to compare the same city at different points in time, but more difficult to compare different cities at the same point in time.

ever reach them at all), but it is possible to calculate changes in wages and salaries bills for some towns and cities between 1970 and 1972. Inflation had not really taken off in this period, but, nevertheless, it was at a higher level than for most of the preceding years going back to 1950. Table 5.6 presents the results of the calculations, and it shows that labour costs were increasing, on average, at a faster rate than current expenditure as a whole. Additional figures for West Germany also show that labour costs rose rapidly as a percentage of total expenditure, 1970-1975, and in Sweden there was a similar increase over the same period. To this extent it seems that the previous conclusion should be modified. Even if mounting labour costs have played no *special* part in the long term rising cost curves of local government, the effect in recent years has been stronger. Increases in wages and salaries appear to have some special connection with the rapid acceleration in local costs in the last ten years.

Two further points based upon the figures in Table 5.6 should be made, however. First, there is no consistent pattern for all towns and countries. While there is an average increase in salaries and wages as a proportion of total current expenditure, there is also a decrease in some towns and cities, showing that labour costs have not always gone up as fast as the other costs. Second, the relationship between the costs of an increased labour force, and other local government costs is a complex and variable one. While the nineteen cities listed in Tables 5.3 and 5.6 increased their labour force by an average of 5.4% between 1970 and 1972, wages and salaries as a proportion of current expenditure increased by an average of only 1.3% in the same period. Bodo, in Norway, for example, added almost one worker in six to its labour force, but salaries and wages as a proportion of current expenditure increased by only one Kroner in forty.

These two qualifications appear to support the conclusion that while the extra costs of labour are not inconsiderable, they do not seem to be as powerful as many writers have assumed; labour costs have increased, but they have not increased all that much faster than other costs, even in years as recent as 1970-1972. Consequently, the labour intensity of local government has contributed to its rising costs, and it seems to have played a significant role in recent years, but, at the same time, it is necessary to look for additional factors if we are to reach a more complete understanding of the causes of rising expenditure.

Capital costs and debt charges

It is widely held in local government circles that this level of government suffers, by comparison with other parts of the public sector, from being capital intensive, and from having to pay out large sums of money to service its capital debt, especially during inflationary periods when interest rates tend to be high. At first sight it may seem odd to claim that local government is capital intensive immediately after showing that it is labour intensive. In most people's minds, capital intensity and labour intensity are mutually exclusive categories, so that local government can be either one or the other, but not both. In the public sector, however, there is a third type of expenditure which consists of transfers to the private sector, or to other public bodies. A large proportion of central government expenditure, for example, consists of pensions and social security payments of various kinds, and of grants to other public or quasi-public bodies. Local government in many (but not all countries) spends relatively small amounts in financial transfers of this kind and can, therefore, be both capital and labour intensive, by comparison with other parts of the public sector. And indeed this is the case for all six countries covered in this study, where a higher proportion of local than of central government expenditure comes under the capital account (see Table 5.7). The precise definition of capital expenditure varies from country to country and, indeed, from one authority to another within a country, but in general the term is taken to cover spending on assets such as machinery, buildings, and plant, which continues to have a value long after it is acquired.

Given that local government is capital intensive, is there any indication that it suffers from mounting debt charges on its capital borrowings? The information in Table 5.7 shows that there are marked variations between countries in this respect. In Denmark, Norway and Sweden not only has capital spending declined, as a percentage of total expenditure, but loan charges (debt repayment and interest charges) have also declined as a percentage of current expenditure. (The figure for Sweden does not represent the real state of affairs because some municipalities have formed 'private' corporations in order to avoid central government regulations on capital expenditure.) In Italy and the UK, in contrast, capital spending has also declined as a proportion of total expenditure, but debt charges have increased as a proportion of current expenditure. And in West Germany, in spite of fluctuations from

Table 5.7
Capital intensity and debt charges

Denmark				
Local debt charges as a % of local current expenditure	1966/7:	11.6	1976/7:	2.1
Central government interest payments as a % of central current expenditure			1972:	1.4
Local capital expenditure as a % of total local expenditure		16.6	1976/7:	10.2
Central government capital expenditure as a % of total expenditure			1972:	5.8
Italy				
Local debt charges as a % of total local expenditure	1970:	27.2	1975:	33.0
Central government interest payment as a % of total central expenditure	1951:	6.0	1973:	7.0
Capital expenditure as a % of total expenditure:				
Total public sector	1951:	16.7	1972:	9.6
Communes		18.1		15.3
Norway				
Municipal capital expenditure as a % of total local expenditure:				
Urban communes	1962:	27.9	1971:	24.9
Local communes		26.0		25.5
Central government capital expenditures as a % of total central expenditure	1972:	4.8	1974:	4.5
Municipal debt charges as a % of total local expenditure:				
Urban communes	1962:	12.3	1974:	6.8
Rural communes		6.4		3.6
Central government debt charges as a % of total central expenditure		12.9		4.0
Sweden				
Municipal capital expenditure as a % of total expenditure	1955:	26.3	1975:	14.2
State capital expenditure as a % of total expenditure	1958:	13.3		7.8

Table 5.7 (continued)

Sweden (continued)				
Central government interest payments as a % of central current expenditure	1956:	3.6	1977:	4.7
UK				
Local government capital expenditure as a % of total expenditure	1965:	30.3	1975:	23.5
Central government capital expenditure as a % of total expenditure		15.4		16.4
Local government debt interest as a % of current expenditure	1950/1:	12.9		16.8
Central government debt interest as a % of current expenditure	1965:	10.4		7.1
West Germany				
Local government capital expendit-ture as a % of total expenditure	1950:	33.2	1973:	42.5
Central government capital expenditure as a % of total expenditure	1972:	9.3	1974:	8.0
Local government debt charges as a % of total income	1950:	0.8	1973:	8.0
Central government interest payments as a % of total income		1.0	1976:	4.3

one year to the next, capital spending and debt charges are higher now than in 1950. It would seem, therefore, that not all local government systems carry the same burden of capital charges. Why is this?

First, there is the fact that countries vary quite considerably in their degree of capital intensity. Capital spending now accounts for between a tenth and a seventh of total outgoings in Denmark, Sweden and Italy, a quarter in Norway and the UK and over 40% in West Germany, where local government is responsible for many capital intensive services, and has sustained a relatively heavy investment programme ever since 1950. Second, while interest rates have increased in almost every country over the past twenty years, especially in the 1970s, they still vary considerably from one country to another. The exact interest paid by local government on its borrowings is difficult to ascertain: it varies over time, according to the type of loan, and even from one local authority to another in the same country. But a rough idea of interest rates may be gained from Table 5.8

Table 5.8
Central government bond yields
(Average yields to maturity on issues with at least 12 years life in % per annum)

	1951	*1960*	*1970*	*1978 (Feb.)*
Denmark	N.A.	N.A.	10.6	13.2
Italy	6.1	5.2	9.0	14.1
Norway	N.A.	N.A.	6.3	8.4
Sweden	3.2	4.6	7.4	9.9
UK	3.8	5.4	9.2	11.8
West Germany	N.A.	6.4*	8.3	5.4

* Covers bonds of all public authorities, including some with lives of less than 12 years.
N.A. = not available
Source: International Monetary Fund, *International Financial Statistics,* Washington, interest rate tables for appropriate years.

These figures show that a borrowing requirement of the given level in 1978 would probably cost least in West Germany, more in Norway and Sweden, and most in Denmark, the UK and Italy. With the exception of West Germany, however, interest rates were higher in 1978 than in 1970.

Third, although it is not possible to obtain statistics, different countries raise varying proportions of their capital expenditure from loans, and the proportions vary over time according to economic circumstances. Authorities with a surplus of revenue income over expenditure may well decide to use it on capital projects, but authorities which are not allowed to budget for a surplus, or which have little extra after all revenue commitments have been met, may have to borrow large amounts of money to finance capital expenditure. In addition, the arguments for borrowing in certain circumstances are fairly strong: in inflationary periods it may reduce the cost of capital expenditure in the long run (since inflation reduces the value of money), although it may also result in high interest payments in the short run; it serves to spread capital costs over a period of time, which is consistent with the actual value of capital items; and last, since capital assets are created for the benefit of future taxpayers (as well as present ones) it seems only reasonable that they should help to pay for them. The power of these arguments varies according to economic circumstances, however, and so also do the borrowing requirements of different local government systems.

If we can infer from the state of local finances as they are described in Chapter 1, and summarized in Table 1.4, it would seem likely that Italy's borrowing requirements are highest, followed by the UK's, and then by West Germany's. Those of the three Scandinavian countries are likely to be lowest.

In other words, the burden of local government's capital intensity seems to depend upon three main variables — the degree of capital intensity, the interest rate, and local authority borrowing requirements. Table 5.9 summarizes the relative state of affairs in the six countries, albeit in an over-simplified manner.

Table 5.9
Three determinants in the debt burden in six countries

	Capital intensity (compared with other countries)	*Interest rate*	*Borrowing requirements*
Denmark	Lowest	Medium	Low and decreasing
Italy	Low	Highest	Highest and increasing
Norway	High	Lowest	Low and decreasing
Sweden	Medium to low	Medium to low	Low and decreasing
UK	High	High	High and increasing
West Germany	Highest	Low	Medium and increasing

The table helps to explain why three Scandinavian countries have relatively few financial problems with their capital expenditure. Their low borrowing requirements combine with either a low interest rate or a low capital intensity. At the other extreme a high borrowing requirement in Italy, combined with the highest interest rates, but a relatively low capital intensity, generates quite severe debt and interest payment problems. In between the Scandinavian and Italian extremes fall the UK and Germany, the latter with a heavy capital programme and a growing need to borrow, and the former with relatively high interest rates, capital intensity, and borrowing requirements. In other words, it is not capital intensity which is important, but the way in which borrowing requirements (only tenuously connected with capital spending) combine with other financial considerations to generate debt charges. Norwegian communes are more capital intensive than Italian communes, for example, but finances are such that debt charges are relatively low and decreasing in the former, large and increasing in the latter. With this in mind, it is worth examining the contribution of capital expenditure and debt charges towards rising local government costs in Italy, the UK, and West Germany in greater detail.

Capital expenditure and debt charges in the UK, Germany and Italy

In the UK capital expenditure and debt charges have had a highly significant effect in increasing local government costs. The effect is highlighted by the information given in Table 5.10 which compares the changes in public sector, in central government, and in local government expenditure for the ten-year period between 1964 and 1974. While local spending has grown at a faster rate than either total public or central government spending, the difference narrows when debt interest is excluded from the calculations. But when debt interest alone is compared, the difference widens to its greatest proportions — local government debt interest increased by no less than 322% between 1965 and 1975, whereas central government's increased by only 126%. At the same time, local government's capital expenditure increased at a slower rate than central government's, although its total debt grew considerably faster. In short, while local government has not expanded its capital investment as fast as central government, the amount it pays in debt interest has grown considerably faster, and so has the size of its total debt. As a consequence, debt interest accounted for only 7.1% of the central government's current account in 1975, but for 16.8% of local government's current account.

This state of affairs seems best explained by three related factors. To start with, local government is not only more capital intensive than central government, but it also finances a considerably higher proportion of its capital spending through loans — 73% as against

Table 5.10

Total percentage increases in expenditure and debt, UK 1964 to 1974

	Total public sector	*Central government*	*Local government*
Total expenditure	226	223	245
Current expenditure	229	222	268
	(central plus local government)		
Current expenditure excluding debt interest	232	235	256
Debt interest	176	126	322
Capital expenditure	168	233	195
Public debt	62	33	153

Source: Calculated from data in Central Statistical Office, *Annual Abstract of Statistics, 1975,* London: HMSO, 1976, pp. 316-17, 326, 352.

Note: Central government expenditure excludes transfers to local government.

central government 48%. Between 1969 and 1973, local government's total borrowing requirements were £7,564 million, while central government's was only £2,235 million. And this in spite of the fact that central government spent two and a quarter times as much as local government! Central government's slender borrowing requirements were, in turn, due to its surplus of some £18,000 million between 1969 and 1973. Local government cannot budget for a surplus in the UK. In the second place, local government's interest rates on its mounting debt have risen steadily from an average of 3.09% in 1950 to 6.44% in 1972, and to 9.77% in 1976.

The third explanation lies in the growth of short term borrowing on the part of local authorities. They have powers to borrow temporarily while they wait for the receipt of revenues or an authorized loan, and local authorities have entered the short term money market in a big way during the last decade, as reflected in the growth in the figures in the table which follows.

Table 5.11
Short-term borrowing in the UK
(£ million)

	Total	*Up to 7 days*	*7 days to 3 months*	*3-12 months*
1961	933	558	229	146
1968	2,073	1,545	311	217
1975	3,800	2,400	500	900

Sources: Alberta Sbragia, 'Public Policy Decision-Making Constraints: Local Government Borrowing in the US, UK and France,' (Paper given to the Annual Meeting of the American Political Science Association, September 1976, p. 17), and evidence by the Bank of England to the Committee of Inquiry into Local Government Finance, Appendix 6, *The Relationship Between Central and Local Government,* London: HMSO, 1976, p. 2.

These short term debts are in addition to the long term debts which have been increasing by £70 million per annum over the last few years. By mid-1975 the total was £969 million. One conclusion can be drawn safely from this array of figures: the capital intensity of local government, combined with its need to borrow large amounts, has contributed substantially to the steep rise in costs, and may well be the single most important factor of all those discussed for the UK so far.

The same conclusion emerges from an examination of the West German situation. Germany is alone among the six countries in having a high level of capital expenditure which has not fallen a great deal in the recent past. Indeed, for a period in the early 1960s, capital spending accounted for more than half of total outgoings (it will be remembered that the Länder pay teachers' salaries, and, therefore, take a considerable load off the local current account), and even in the 1970s this figure has not dropped below 40%, compared with 10% in Denmark, and 14% in Sweden. The sheer size of this investment programme means that, in spite of low interest rates, debt charges have mounted steadily from less than 1% of total expenditure in 1960 to more than 8% in 1973. The full significance of local authority debts can be judged from the following figures.

Table 5.12
The public debt in West Germany

	Public debt as a % of GNP	*Percentage of the public debt owed by:* Federal government and special funds	Länder	Local government
1950	18.2	30.8	67.1	2.1
1972	18.7	40.2	23.8	36.0

Not only has the local debt multiplied faster than that of other levels of government, but local debts have also grown as a proportion of total income from 5.9% in 1950 to 11.9% in 1973. In short, in West Germany, as in the UK, borrowing requirements and debt charges have increased at a faster rate than local government spending as a whole, and have, therefore, contributed disproportionately to the ever increasing expansion of local expenses.

By comparison with this, Italy is a very special case. Although Italian communes do not spend a high proportion of their total budget on capital projects, their gross investment expenditure grew faster than that of the total public sector between 1960 and 1971, after which the rate of growth dropped a little.

Table 5.13
The growth of gross investment expenditure in Italy

	Consumer price index	*Total public sector investment*	*Investment of communes*
1960	100	100	100
1965	188	138	175
1968	100	100	100
1972	119	173	169

In addition, to cope with ever increasing deficits in their annual budgets, communes were permitted to borrow from both public and private institutions, not only to cover investment expenditure but also to meet their deficits on the current side of their accounts. By 1970, loans contributed over half of total local income, and by 1975, it was about two-thirds. This would be a heavy burden in any country, but in Italy the whole situation is made still worse by high interest rates — roughly twice as high as Norway's and anything up to three times as high as Germany's. Consequently, debt charges consumed over half of current expenditure in 1970, and over two-thirds in 1975. If they have not already got there, Italian communes will soon be in the position of having to borrow not merely to cover capital expenditure, or even to cover some current deficits, but in order to pay interest charges on previous loans.

Land and construction costs

It seems probable that substantial increases in the cost of land and of building in the last decade will have contributed significantly to the ever increasing expenditure of local government, which, in many countries, is heavily involved in various kinds of construction work and in purchasing rather large quantities of land. Unfortunately, evidence on this point is rather hard to come by and, consequently, the figures in Table 5.14 are somewhat meagre and inconclusive, although there is some information to work on. In Norway, for example, the cost of building houses has risen faster than the consumer price index, and public works expenditure in the urban communes has also increased at a faster pace than total expenditure. Moreover, since public works expenditure accounts for

Table 5.14
Land and building costs of local government

Norway				
Public works expenditure as % of total current expenditure constant prices (1966 = 100)				
Urban communes	1962:	12.3	1975:	16.9
Index		100		238
Building cost index, (1968 = 100)				
Block of flats	1960:	63	1976:	199
Wooden house		64		201
Consumer price index	1967:	100	1975:	176
UK				
Cost of traditionally built 1 or 2 storey local authority houses (1966 = 100)	1964:	92	1972:	170
Land prices (1966 = 100)		84		268
West Germany				
Local authority land purchases as % of total expenditure	1950:	1.6	1973:	3.9
Cost of major construction projects as % of total expenditure		17.1		25.8
Index for general construction (1965 = 100)	1965:	100	1975:	180

almost a sixth of total spending, any increases in the costs of this item are bound to have a big effect on the total local government bill.

In the UK, the costs of building local authority housing have also risen steeply, although it is land which has responded most quickly to economic circumstances by doubling and then trebling its price in less than ten years.[3] The same is true in West Germany where the cost of land purchases has increased more than two and a half times as fast as total local government spending during the post-war period. Overall, land purchases still account for less than 5% of total outgoing, but in some of the big cities which have large building and construction programmes, the price of land has had a significant effect on the cost of local government, more than doubling as a percentage of total expenditure between 1950 and 1973. Major construction costs, on the other hand, comprise no less than a quarter of total expenditure and increased as a proportion of this total by 50% in the period from 1950 and 1973. This, of course, is another aspect of the capital intensity of West German local government, and it is doubtful whether other countries have been so strongly affected by rising land prices and construction costs. The Norwegian and British evidence, however, suggests that less capital intensive local government systems have also suffered to some extent from increases in these costs.

Public consumption expenditure

The essential argument of this chapter is that local spending has risen particularly quickly over the past few decades, and especially during the recent period of high inflation, because local government is the prisoner of a variety of economic circumstances over which it has little or no control. This is the crux of the problem so far as local costs are concerned, and it may be summed up by examining what is termed the public consumption expenditure of local government. For the purposes of this study public consumption expenditure represents the *direct* demand for local goods and services, including salaries and wages, and the cost of maintaining and repairing capital equipment. It does not include transfers to the public or private sectors, or capital expenditure, or debt charges. The point about public consumption expenditure is that it is relatively inelastic, and, therefore, sensitive to changes in prices. In other words, salaries and wages have to be paid, schools and houses have to be repaired, and roads have to be maintained. Local government can cut its costs in the short run by reducing repair and maintenance standards, but before long economies are usually overtaken by heavy repair costs, and the savings turn into losses.

The point can be illustrated by comparing the costs of maintaining a building, as a form of public consumption expenditure, and the costs of paying old age pensions, as a form of transfer. If the roof of the building starts to leak, then officials are faced with the choice of repairing it, or leaving it untouched. In the latter case, the building is likely to fall into increasing disrepair, to become uninhabitable, and eventually to require demolition, or very expensive repairs. Thus, cuts in this year's repair bill are likely to cause more than proportionate increases in next year's bill. The same is not true of pensions. Politicians face continual pressure to increase pensions (as they do to maintain public buildings in good repair), but any delay in increases represents a net gain to the public purse. In economic terms it generally pays officials to repair as soon as possible, and to delay pension increases for as long as possible, and to this extent they have less control over the former than the latter. By and large public consumption expenditure, since it is a direct demand on goods and services, is less amenable to reduction, and, therefore, its total is likely to increase relatively rapidly during inflationary periods.

As Table 5.15 shows, public consumption expenditure constitutes a higher proportion of total outgoings for local than for central government. This helps to explain why costs have risen faster than for central government.

Conclusion

There is some fairly good evidence to show that local government costs have risen faster than other costs in many Western European nations, particularly during the last decade of high inflation. The increase is due, in part, to the labour intensity of local government, but the evidence suggests that this factor has been rather overemphasized, since it seems that the wages and salaries bill of local government has risen faster than other costs only in the last few

Table 5.15
Public consumption expenditure as a percentage of total local and central government spending

		Local government		*Central government*
Denmark[1]	1973/4	40.4		34.1
	1974/5	41.8		28.0
Italy[2]	1950/1	61.6		46.7
	1972/3	53.9		35.6
Norway[2]	1950	32.2		32.3
	1977	50.0		46.9
Sweden[2]	1961	63.0*	1961/2	25.6
	1976	76.9		27.2
UK[2]	1966	48.1		30.1
	1976	50.6		32.6
West Germany	1961	31.7		33.9
	1975	35.3		28.7

Notes: 1. Public consumption equals salaries and wages of employees plus intermediate consumption (e.g. the purchase of goods and services) minus sales of non-commodity determined goods and services.

2. Public consumption equals total expenditure minus transfers to individuals or the private sector, and minus investments. Transfers include debt charges and repayments of capital loans.

* Estimate.

years. Labour intensity has accelerated the underlying tendency for local expenditure to increase, but over the whole post-war period it seems to be one of many factors and not a dominant one. It seems to have played a more important role in the last decade when inflation may well have caused labour costs to rise relatively sharply.

Nor is capital intensity directly related to rapidly rising costs, for in some countries where local government is heavily capital intensive (Norway compared with Italy, for example), the resource squeeze is not particularly tight. Rather, it is a country's local government borrowing requirement combined with the interest rate on loans which is important. In this respect, the three countries with the tightest squeeze — Italy, the UK and West Germany — have been hard hit by a need to borrow more and more, combined with an increase in interest rates. Borrowing at relatively high interest rates is important in more ways than one; not only is it expensive, but the expense is usually maintained over a period of years. Moreover, costs escalate rapidly as old loans at low rates of interest are replaced with new loans at high rates.

There is also some evidence to suggest that a relatively steep rise in the costs of land and building have played their part in pushing up the costs of local government in Norway, the UK and West Germany, particularly in the latter's larger cities which have spent large amounts on urban renewal and development. And finally, the evidence shows that public consumption expenditure accounts for a higher proportion of local than central government spending, and it seems that public consumption expenditure is more likely to rise with inflation than other forms of public expenditure.

Overall, the evidence shows fairly clearly that inflation has had a stronger effect on local costs compared with central government. Consequently the costs of producing services at a given level have been borne upon a rising tide over which local government has very little control. For some countries where inflation has barely reached double figures this has not presented an acute problem, but for others, such as Italy and the UK, where inflation has exceeded 20%, the extra financial burdens placed upon local government have been considerable. Cuts not only in capital but also in current spending have helped to reduce the strain, but this has usually been at the expense of reduced service quantity and quality, and in some cases it has not prevented costs rising fast, even if they have not risen as fast as they would have done without the cuts. In these countries much depends upon the future rate of inflation and the effectiveness of central government policy in keeping it down. At best, capital costs may continue at a relatively high level until the effects of high inflation have worked through the system. At worst, costs may rise still more, provoking a further round of expenditure cuts and a further deterioration of services.

NOTES

1. Council of Europe, *The Financial Structures of Local and Regional Authorities in Europe*, Study Series on Local and Regional Authorities in Europe, Number 13, Vol. II, Strasbourg, 1976, p. 72.

2. One country for which the relevant data are available is the United States. In his analysis of the financial crisis in New York City Donald Haider writes: 'Inflation has been the greatest single cause of increased city expenditures. The price paid for goods and services by state and local governments rose at an average rate of 4.2 per cent annually between 1955 and 1970 compared with 3.6 percent for the federal government and 2.7 per cent for the economy as a whole. As an aggregate of all general expenditures during this time, inflation accounted for well over 40 per cent of the total increase in outlays'. (Donald H. Haider, 'Fiscal Scarcity: A New Urban Perspective', in: Louis H. Masotti and Robert L. Lineberry, eds., *The New Urban Politics*, Cambridge, Mass.: Ballinger, 1976, p. 176.)

3. For more detailed evidence see Valerie A. Karn, *Housing Standards and Costs*, University of Birmingham, Centre for Urban and Regional Studies, Occasional Paper 25, 1973, pp. 41-7.

6

Income and Property Taxes: Problems of Visibility, Buoyancy and Fairness

Introduction

The local resource squeeze is caused not only by rapidly rising expenditure but also by a relatively inelastic set of sources of local income. The differences between a fixed property tax and an income tax are particularly important in this respect, and it is notable that the three local government systems which derive a relatively large proportion of their income from an income tax — Denmark, Norway, and Sweden — have the least severe financial problems, even though local spending in these countries has risen rapidly during the post-war period. The yield of an income tax tends to rise with inflation, whereas the yield of a fixed property tax tends to decline in real terms during inflationary periods. Property taxes have the added disadvantage of high visibility and unpopularity. Although West Germany and Italy both use a local income tax to some extent, they do so less than the Scandinavian countries in this study, and a close examination of their methods of raising local income shows weakness and deficiencies in the system. Local authorities in Britain have the considerable disadvantage of having to rely on a fixed property tax as their only way of raising local revenues.

Limitations on income: the other side of the resource squeeze

Increasing expenditure, no matter how hard and fast it may climb, will not create financial problems as long as income rises at the same pace. Or, to put the point in a slightly different way, the resource squeeze is the creation of two sets of contradictory pressures upon expenditure and upon income. The income side of the resource squeeze is no less crucial than the expenditure side, and it is to this income that we now turn.

Of course, in a world in which scarce resources constrain almost every form of human activity, all societies and their governments, and all parts of society whether they are small families, or huge corporations, must face the fact that income is strictly limited. But the important fact so far as local government is concerned is that local authorities in some countries seem to have a rather more elastic source of income than others, and are able to accommodate fairly large expenditure increases without a great deal of strain. By comparison, the income of local authorities in other countries appears to be strictly limited, so that it takes a great deal more political will and effort to ensure that income keeps pace with expenditure.

Perhaps the most simple and obvious explanation of these differences is the fact that countries differ not only in their wealth, but also in their ability to generate new wealth to pay for expanding local government services. It seems reasonable to suggest that countries with booming economies can afford to spend more on local services, while stagnant or less dynamic ones cannot. Unfortunately, this neat and simple explanation does not quite fit the facts. For example, Italy, with local financial problems of crisis proportions, had a rate of economic growth which was marginally higher than Denmark's during the period from 1963 to 1974. And Germany, with worse local financial problems than Sweden, had a growth rate which was appreciably higher than Sweden's. Of the six nations, those with the worst resource squeeze (Italy and the UK) ranked at the top and the bottom of the league table for economic growth.[1] These figures suggest that the financial problems of local government are not simply a reflection of national economic conditions. In fact, they suggest that the link between the two is rather tenuous.

Nor is it simply a matter of increases in local expenditure outpacing increases in national income, for a quick examination of the basic statistics produced in Table 1.2 in the opening chapter will show that local spending has increased appreciably faster than GNP in some countries with the healthiest local finances. Conversely, some of the countries with the most acute problems have expanded the local sector only slowly relative to GNP. For example, in Norway and Sweden public expenditure rose (respectively) from 13% and 11% of GNP in 1950, to 21% and 24% by 1974/5. In contrast, it took from 1950 to 1976 for local spending in the UK to increase from 10.6% to 17.1% of GNP. And in West Germany local spending rose from only 6.5% to 9.5% of GNP in the quarter century after 1950. The figures show that the severity of local financial problems are not simply or directly a function of wider economic conditions.

Another factor which might help to explain variations in the health of local finances in different countries is the extent to which they have to rely upon their own financial resources in raising their income. This theory suggests that in the complex world of the twentieth century, where both public and private finances tend to be increasingly centralized on national governments and capital cities, local governments can no longer afford to rely upon their own resources. They must, increasingly, depend upon central government because it is the main centre of financial management and the main source of public finance. To the extent that local government pays its own way with its own locally derived revenues, it is bound (the theory suggests) to run into economic problems sooner or later.

The theory carries a good deal of common sense appeal, for it is certainly true that financial control is becoming increasingly centralized and concentrated in national institutions, just as central governments are paying a larger and larger proportion of the local government bill through grants and financial transfers of one kind or another. Unfortunately, however, the theory does not fit the facts, at least so far as the six nations in this study are concerned. Norway and Sweden rely heavily on local sources of income, whereas Italy is almost wholly dependent upon non-local sources, although loans distort the picture in this case. In contrast, the UK relies heavily upon central government grants, while Danish municipalities receive a relatively small proportion of their income in the form of central government grants, although they also receive large sums of money in the form of 100% refunds for certain specified services. Overall, the figures in Table 6.1 in no way suggest that dependence upon local sources of income contributes to the severity of the resource squeeze.

Table 6.1
Local and other sources of gross local government income

		Local sources	*Grants from higher authorities*	*Other sources*
		%	%	%
Denmark	1976/7	37	58	5
Italy	1975	5	25	70
Norway	1975	75	19	6
Sweden	1975	70	24	6
UK	1976	39	44	17
West Germany	1973	48	27	25

Notes: 1. Local sources include mainly local taxes and the fees and charges levied for local services. It does not include loans.
2. In some countries a small proportion of local income is derived from a tax which is shared with another level of government. Local government's share of this is counted as a local source of income.
3. In all countries a large proportion of non-local income is made up of grants from higher level government.

Income tax and property tax: the problems of buoyancy and visibility

The main theme of this chapter is that the capacity of local authorities to increase their income is closely tied up with the types of taxes which they have at their disposal. Local governments in some countries have a range of taxes which provide them with a relatively elastic source of income, while others, with a different mix or range of taxes, find themselves with an income which is relatively fixed. The elasticity of a tax is, in turn, partly dependent upon its buoyancy during inflationary periods (a theme which is widely discussed by economists), and partly dependent upon the visibility of the tax, a factor which is based largely upon political considerations, and which has not been adequately discussed by political scientists. These two concepts of buoyancy and visibility are important to an understanding of local finances, and must be considered carefully.

By the visibility of a tax is meant the extent to which people are aware of its existence, the fact that they are paying it, and the amount (roughly) that they pay. By and large income tax, purchase tax, VAT, and duty on petrol, tobacco, and spirits are relatively invisible, either because the amount is hidden in the price of the goods, or because the tax is extracted at source. The visibility of the same tax, however, varies from one country to another. In some parts of Scandinavia, for example, the amount of income tax paid to both central and local government by individual citizens is public knowledge, and is even published in newspapers. In other countries income tax is less visible. Though people may be aware of paying the less visible taxes, many are not acutely conscious of their existence, and would be surprised if the total amount they pay each year was added up for them. In contrast there is a range of more visible taxes, the most significant of which, from a local government point of view, is the tax on land and property. These taxes are generally based upon the capital value of property, but in the UK they are based upon its annual rental value.

Property taxes are generally more visible than income tax or purchase tax for several reasons. First, the property owner is sent a tax demand every so often which means that he knows exactly how much tax he pays. In contrast, to calculate how much VAT one pays in any given year on ordinary household purchases is quite a complicated business, and few people have the knowledge, the time, or the incentive to do so. Second, property taxes are paid out of disposable income, a rather painful business by comparison with the payment of taxes at source. And third, property taxes are not infrequently paid in a lump sum monthly, twice yearly, or even yearly. Less visible taxes are paid in smaller amounts every week or month, or as goods are bought across the shop counter. For these reasons taxpayer resistance to visible taxes, such as property taxes, is likely to be greater than that for relatively invisible taxes, such as

VAT and income tax. While few people actually like paying taxes, their resistance to visible taxes is likely to be more emphatic and determined than their resistance to less visible taxes.

Property taxes have a further important disadvantage. While income tax is usually buoyant in the sense that its yield increases as incomes increase, property taxes are usually fixed, and they yield the same amount each year. This means that income tax will automatically keep abreast of inflation without any adjustment to the tax rate. In fact, if income tax is progressive, its yield in real terms may actually increase during inflationary periods because increases in income will move some people into a higher tax bracket. The yield of a fixed property tax will normally decrease during inflationary periods, unless the property is revalued, or the tax rate is increased. Some countries find it expensive, time consuming, and administratively cumbersome to revalue property regularly, which means that the tax rate has to be increased in order to keep pace with inflation. But since the property tax tends to be highly visible, any increase in the rate of taxation will tend to meet with taxpayers' resistance. It should be emphasized once again that most people do not like paying taxes, and that an increase in any tax rate will meet with resistance, but highly visible taxes will tend to generate most resistance.

Resistance to increases in property tax rates are likely to be further strengthened by the fact that it is easy to confuse an increase in tax rates with a real increase in the amount of taxation. As already pointed out, property taxes are usually fixed, which means that during inflationary periods the tax rate has to be increased if the tax is to maintain its real yield. However, taxpayers often believe that an increase in the tax rate means paying more in real terms. In actual fact, if the tax rate is increased by less than the inflation rate, their taxes will actually decrease in real terms. Few property taxpayers appreciate this point, however, and consequently they tend to oppose *any* increase, whether it is real or merely apparent.

There is the further point that one of the most important psychological aspects of a tax may be not its rate in absolute terms, so much as this year's change in the tax rate. In other words, it may be increases in taxes, even where these are marginal changes, which attract most public attention and the greatest amount of taxpayers' resistance. Apart from anything else, the media tend to concentrate on tax increases, and the general public's dislike of taxes is often regenerated by such increases, which take on a special symbolic importance. In short, the most visible and politically sensitive thing about a tax may not be its rate, but the most recent change in the tax rate. This is a further disadvantage for fixed property taxes.

And lastly, there is sometimes a problem about the fairness of property taxes in the mind of the general public. Income is often regarded as a fair basis for taxation, while property is not. The following sort of argument is typically produced: compare two houses of identical size and value, and taxed at the same rate, one of which is occupied by four wage earners, and the other by a retired couple. The disposable income of the latter may be no more than a fraction of the former, but the two households pay the same amount in local property taxes. It might be pointed out that they will invariably pay very different amounts in total taxation, just as it might be claimed that the retired couple should pay property taxes based upon the value of the house they occupy, but, nevertheless, many people seem to feel that the tax on the pensioners is unjust. This sort of feeling adds to the unpopularity of property taxes.

The conclusion must be, therefore, that any local authority which raises a large proportion of its income from an income tax, or which does not have to rely heavily upon a property tax, is at an advantage. And the steeper the rate of inflation, the greater their advantage. In other words, all other things being equal, a municipality which uses an income tax to generate a large proportion of its finances is likely to have less of a resource squeeze than one which has no income tax, or which relies heavily upon a fixed property tax.

These are precisely the circumstances of the three Scandinavian countries in this survey. As the figures in Table 6.2 show, local government in Norway, Denmark, and Sweden relies very heavily upon an income tax. In fact, in all three countries, the tax is by far and away the largest source of locally derived revenue, and, with the exception of Denmark, it contributes the largest proportion of income from any source. In the case of Denmark, the amount received from income tax is exceeded only by central government grants. In the UK, on the other hand, local government is not allowed to levy an income tax of any kind, while German municipalities derived little more than a seventh of their total

Table 6.2
Sources of local authority gross income, 1972

	Denmark	*Italy*	*Norway*	*Sweden*	*UK*	*West Germany*
	%	%	%	%	%	%
Local taxes						
General tax on goods and services		10.4				
Taxes on specific goods and services	0.7	7.1		0.1		0.6
Income tax	33.4		48.0	42.1		13.8
Corporation tax		1.7	2.6	3.6		
Land/property tax	3.9	2.3	1.3		33.8	4.0
Other recurrent property taxes	0.5	3.9	2.1			
Commercial tax		31.5				14.8(1)
Other mixed taxes	0.9	1.7				
Taxes on real estate transactions		1.1				1.1
Sub-total	39.4	59.7	54.0	45.8	33.8	34.3
Grants						
Specific grants	55.8	7.0	11.3	21.7	4.4	16.4
General grants	1.1	1.0	3.6	3.4	41.6	13.2(2)
Sub-total	56.9	8.0	14.9	25.1	49.0	29.6
Other						
Interest and dividends	1.7	1.2	1.0	1.1	1.8	1.6
Returns of local public enterprises		22.8			1.9	0.3
Charges for services		1.6	26.7	}	}	29.0
				28.0	16.5	
Sundry returns	2.0	6.7	3.4	}	}	5.2(3)
Total	100.0	100.0	100.0	100.0	100.0	100.0(4)

(1) Includes tax on employers.
(2) Includes assigned taxes.
(3) Includes transfers and loan repayments from private sector.
(4) Excludes financial transactions.

Source: Council of Europe, Study Series on Local and Regional Authorities in Europe, No. 13, Volume II, *Financial Apportionment and Equalisation*, Strasbourg, 1976, p. 43.

Note: Denmark moved increasingly to general grants in the 1970s. It is also important to emphasize the fact that different accounting practices in the six nations make it difficult to compare the amounts they raise from local public enterprises and charges. This matter is discussed in greater detail in Chapter 7.

revenues from a tax on personal incomes. Italian communes raised a certain amount of revenue from income taxes after 1974 but, as we shall see, they suffered rather than gained from this arrangement.

The figures in Table 6.2 also indicate that the distribution of property taxes are important, for while none of the Scandinavian countries relies at all heavily upon a property tax, local authorities in the UK have this tax, and this tax alone, at their disposal. In fact, the UK is unique among the countries of Western Europe in this respect. According to the Council of Europe study from which Table 6.2 is taken, no other country in Western Europe relies for more than 8 or 9% of its income upon property tax, and in most cases it contributes no more than 5% to gross local authority incomes. These basic figures alone are enough to suggest a close link between the severity of the local resource squeeze and the type of taxes available to local authorities. Consequently, the remainder of this chapter will analyze the matter in greater detail, showing how different tax systems are related to the severity of the resource squeeze.

The Scandinavian countries: buoyancy and low visibility income taxes

Denmark, Norway and Sweden may be grouped together not only because they have the fewest financial problems but also because their means of raising an income bear a strong family resemblance. As already stated, all rely heavily upon a local income tax. They also have a flat rate tax rather than a progressive one. That is, the same rate is applied to all incomes within any given local authority, as opposed to a progressive tax in which higher incomes are taxed at a higher rate. It may be that local government gains some benefits from applying a flat rate tax, since the high marginal rates levied by central governments in Scandinavia tend to sensitize high income groups to tax matters. In other words, wealthier people are more likely to be aware of the taxes if they pay a high marginal rate of tax, especially when, as sometimes happens, they believe they get little in return for their money. The flat rate local income tax may help to avoid this psychological problem, particularly since local

Table 6.3
Local income tax as a source of local income in Denmark, Norway and Sweden

Denmark: local income tax as a percentage of net current income

1966/7	36.8
1971/2	38.4
1972/3	32.4
1973/4	33.4
1974/5	33.4
1975/6(1)	36.0
1976/7(1)	34.1

(1) Budget not final figures.

Norway: income tax as a percentage of total municipal revenues

	Rural communes	*Urban communes*
1950	54.1	56.8
1962	57.9	51.8
1971	50.2	50.2

Sweden: municipal taxes (2) as a percentage of local income

1950	51.4
1960	42.4
1970	53.3
1975	53.1

(2) Income taxes constituted 92% of municipal taxes in 1972.

authorities in Norway, Denmark, and Sweden tend to levy relatively low rates of tax compared with central government.

It should be emphasized again at this point that it is the marginal rates of taxation, and particularly the changes in these marginal rates, which are important, and not necessarily the total amount paid by taxpayers. In point of fact, huge amounts of money are raised by local income taxes in the Scandinavian nations, but while local income tax rates are set at 16-23% in our three countries, national tax rates go up to as high as 90% or more, and are highly visible for this reason. A relatively small increase of, say, one half of 1% on the flat rate local tax, may seem rather small, even though they are capable of raising large amounts of money, because a large proportion of the population will pay the extra. A larger increase of, say, 5% on the highest marginal rate of national income tax may seem a great deal, but it may raise relatively small amounts of money. The psychological impact of the latter may well overshadow its economic significance.

Within the Scandinavian pattern, however, there is one difference of importance. In both Sweden and Denmark the local income tax rate is set by local authorities themselves, but in Norway all communes must abide by a maximum rate set by central government. The legal upper limit for municipal income taxes in Norway was set at 15% in 1918 and increased to 17.5% in 1945. After an increase of one half of 1% in 1959 it was again raised to 19% in 1962, to 22% in the early 1970s, and finally to 23% in 1978. In 1955 a lower limit of 14% was also established, and this was also increased until it reached 18% in the 1970s. The present range of 4% is, for all intents and purposes, a mere formality, for all but one of the communes applied the highest rate in 1976, and in 1977 the lone exception (a wealthy suburb of Oslo) also raised its rate to the maximum).

Swedish municipalities are free to set their own rate of income tax with no regulation by the central government. The tax base itself is determined by national legislation, and, of course, local authorities are not free to introduce new forms of tax, but they can increase or decrease their income tax rates, subject only to the constraints of the local economic and political system, and to voluntary agreements about tax rates between central and local government. In 1976, the average income tax rate was 16%, and locally derived revenues, of which income tax provided the lion's share, constituted well over half of total income. Income tax is by far and away the largest single source of local revenue.

In Denmark, where income tax constitutes more than a third of current net income, and is second only to government grants as a source of money, the municipalities are free to set their own income tax rate. It is currently close to 16% on average, but ranges from 14% to 24%. In 1972/3, however, the central government set a maximum rate and immediately the yield of the tax fell from 38.4% to 32.4% of current income. Since then there has been no legal maximum, and income tax has gradually climbed back towards its 1971/2 level as a source of income. The central government sometimes urges them to limit their tax effort, but the municipalities retain the legal freedom to set their own rates.

The ability of Swedish and Danish local authorities to set their own tax levels appears to have an impact on the revenue raising capacity of the tax. As the figures in Table 6.3 show, the tax has increased its importance in Denmark, in spite of the ceiling placed on tax rates in 1972/3, and the consequent decline of its revenues during that particular year. In contrast, income tax in Norway is now rather less important as a source of local income than it was twenty-five years ago. This is due mainly to increases in central grants, but it is possible that these have increased partly because of the ceiling placed on local income tax.

These figures are based on only three cases and, therefore, they cannot prove anything, but they do support the idea that income tax is a relatively buoyant and elastic source of income for local authorities, and that the importance of the tax as a source of local income in Denmark, Norway, and Sweden helps to explain why they have been able to increase expenditures with few growing pains.

Italy: a poor kind of income tax

The question of the visibility of local taxes is not important for Italian communes, at least after the reforms introduced in 1974. Up until then the *imposta di famiglia* (or family tax) was the most important single source of locally derived income. This tax was levied on the total income of families resident in a commune, and was based upon indicators of wealth and income such as the size of the dwelling place, ownership of cars, and so on. As from 1 January 1974, however, the family tax was gradually replaced by an altogether different arrangement whereby the communes take a share of the income tax collected by central government. Local income in Italy, however, had one crippling disadvantage. The communal share of the tax was pegged at the 1972 level of the family tax, with a 10% per annum allowance for inflation, a figure which was reasonable in 1972 when the relevant law was passed, and when economic circumstances in Italy were stable. Since then, however, the country has experienced annual inflation rates of anything up to 25%.

Because revenues from income taxes are effectively pegged at 1972 levels with only small allowances for inflation, the proportion of income derived from local sources has shrunk in a relatively short period, as the following figures show.

Table 6.4
Income and other local taxes as a percentage of local income in Italian communes

	(1) *Share of state income taxes*	(2) *Local taxes*	(3) *(1) plus (2)*
1970	11.3	50.2	61.5
1973	29.5	30.7	60.2
1975	44.1	11.8	55.9

Note: Local income is net of income derived from loans.

The decline apparent in the third column of this table is particularly important since income and other local tax constitute a very large amount of total income when loans are excluded from the calculations. The trend will probably not continue, however, because in 1978 Italian communes gained the right to set their own income tax rates. It is still too early to tell what effect this is likely to have on local finances, although it is likely that they will start to improve to some extent.

Britain: the worst kind of tax

Since Britain has no local tax other than a fixed property tax, local revenues suffer from the dual disadvantage of lack of buoyancy and relatively high visibility. In theory property should be revalued every five years by central government, but in practice the last revaluation took effect in 1973 (before that in 1963) with the consequence that local government is bitterly criticized for its rate increases, the largest proportion of which have been to keep abreast of inflation. As Table 6.5 shows, real increases in the rates before 1975/6 were very small. It should be noted that central government's failure to revalue property results in public criticism of local government rate 'increases'.

So far as the visibility of the rates is concerned, the situation is rather more complicated. Rates are levied on most forms of property, but those on commercial and industrial property are relatively invisible because they can simply be treated as a cost of production, and passed on to the consumer in the price of goods and services. Similarly rates on rented domestic property are often fairly invisible where they are as part of the rent. Rates on owner-occupied domestic property are highly visible since these are often paid as a lump sum out of already taxed income. In fact, the owner-occupier domestic rate is so visible, and other rates are so invisible by comparison, that many owner-occupiers firmly believe that they are the only people who pay rates, a fact which heightens their strong sense of injustice.

All this helps to give local taxes a political significance which is out of all proportion to their economic importance. As Table 6.5 shows, rates account for 3% or less of disposable household income, a sum which represents only 14% of the total national tax yield from all sources, central government taxes consuming approximately fifteen times as much of gross household income, and this before VAT was almost doubled to 15%.[2] And yet over the past decade rates have provoked widespread citizens' protests, caused a defeat in the House of Commons (June 1974) of the Labour Government over the issue of local finances, prompted an announcement of the Conservative Party's intention to abolish the rates, caused the setting up of an official committee of enquiry (Layfield) into local government finances, and generated a considerable vote for ratepayers' parties in some parts of the country.

Table 6.5
Domestic ratepayments as a percentage of personal disposable incomes in England and Wales

1959/60	2.7
1964/5	2.2
1969/70	2.5
1975/6	2.7 (provisional estimate)

Source: Report of the Committee of Inquiry into Local Government Finance (Layfield Committee), Cmnd. 6453, London: HMSO, 1976, p. 43.

Table 6.6
Rates as a percentage of total local government current income in England and Wales

1950/1	33.9
1960/1	33.3
1970/1	26.2
1973/4	24.6

Source: Department of the Environment and Welsh Office, *Local Government Financial Statistics, England and Wales,* London: HMSO, appropriate years.

The visibility, unbuoyancy, and unpopularity of the rates explains their decline as a source of local income in Britain, especially during the last decade of high inflation. In 1950 they contributed fractionally more than a third to total income, in 1960 exactly a third, but by 1970 it was down to 26% and only four years later it was below a quarter (Table 6.6). Britain is no exception to the general rule in this regard. None of the five countries in the study which uses a property tax shows an increase in their yield relative to other forms of income, and in the cases of Denmark, Norway, and West Germany there has been a decrease as great, or greater, than that in Britain (see Table 6.7). This international trend underlines the inelasticity of land and property taxes as a source of local income, and also emphasizes the crucial role of the rates in helping to create the local resource squeeze in Britain.

Table 6.7
Land and property taxes as a percentage of local income

Denmark: land taxes as a percentage of local current income		
1966/7	8.7	
1976/7	2.6	
Italy: land and property taxes as a percentage of total local income		
1972	2.3	
Norway: real estate tax as a percentage of local income		
	Rural communes	*Urban communes*
1950	0.4	5.0
1971	0.6	4.1
Sweden: land and property taxes as a percentage of total local income		
1950	0.0	
1972	0.0	
West Germany: property taxes as a percentage of total local income		
1950	16.3	
1973	3.2	

West Germany

In Germany in the post-war period, the main local taxes were levied on property, business, and trade transactions, in addition to which local government received grants from the Länder and federal government, and raised money by charging fees for services, and by selling licences for various activities. In 1955 and 1956 this system was changed and local government was given the exclusive rights to property, business and trade tax as well as several minor taxes and license fees. This reform was a considerable asset to local government which was able to cover 40% of its expenses from its own sources, and which benefited from the growing economic prosperity through its business and trade tax.

In the early 1960s, however, the drawbacks to this system became increasingly apparent. Industrial and commercial cities had large tax bases compared with other places, but even they were at the mercy of business cycles, and their tendency to spend heavily during periods of prosperity and then retrench financially, contributed to inflationary pressures. Consequently, finances were reformed again in 1969, when local authorities relinquished 40% of their business and trade tax to the Länder, in return for a 14% share of the federal income tax. In addition, a complicated scheme was set up to equalize the financial resources of poorer and richer municipalities. For this reason, and because of economic prosperity during the early 1970s, the financial state of local governments improved considerably, and many of them embarked on large and ambitious investment programmes. However, the recession which followed the oil crisis of 1973 left municipalities short of money once again. Some of them were stuck with immense operating and maintenance charges for newly acquired facilities, city revenues declined with unemployment and the lower level of industrial and business activity, and many were faced with rapidly growing social service costs. Hence the not inconsiderable financial problems faced by local government in Germany at the present time.

These problems would be more severe had Germany not reformed her system of local finances. First, the property tax which contributed more than a sixth of total local government income in 1950 has gradually dwindled until it accounted for barely more than 3% in 1973. At the same time, income tax, introduced in 1970, accounted for almost an eighth of total local income in 1973. Germany thus shares some of the characteristics of the Scandinavian countries, but not all of them — property taxes now play a minor role, but income tax, though important, is not a major source of locally derived income. Moreover, local authorities do not set their own income tax rates, but take a share in the amount gathered by the federal government. With a larger share of this tax, or an income tax of their own, German municipalities might well have as secure an economic foundation as those in Scandinavia. At the same time it should also be pointed out that the big cities with poorer populations (e.g. in the Ruhr) have not benefited from income tax as much as the wealthier cities.

Summary and conclusions

The local resource squeeze is not just the product of a remorseless increase in local government expenditure; it is also caused by a relatively inelastic set of local taxes. Local expenditure in Denmark, Norway, and Sweden has risen rapidly over the past decade, but this has created relatively few serious growing pains for local government. On the contrary, Scandinavian municipalities have increased their income as quickly as their expenditure. By comparison, local government expenditure in the UK has risen less rapidly, but this increase has caused a much more serious set of financial problems.

One of the main reasons for this difference lies in the sources of income of local government in the two countries. Danish authorities are rather a special case since they derive a fairly substantial portion of their income from central government refunds which cover the total cost of certain services and pensions. However, Danish authorities also levy an income tax, and have the power to set their own rate of taxation, whereas the only tax available to British local government is a property tax known as the rates. Not only does an income tax tend to be less politically visible in some countries, but most forms of the tax are inflation-proof in the sense that their yield tends to keep pace with inflation. Its lack of political visibility also means that it is less likely to generate severe taxpayers' resistance, compared with land and property taxes, which are quite often associated with taxpayers' revolts — that in California being the latest and one of the most spectacular examples. Property taxes suffer from the further disadvantages that they are sometimes regarded as a rather unfair form of taxation.

The last general point to be made about forms of taxation is that marginal rates of tax, and especially changes in marginal rates, seem to assume a disproportionate significance in the mind of many taxpayers. To take marginal rates first, the Scandinavian municipalities which levy a relatively low, standard rate income tax (16-23%) may have a psychological advantage over their national governments which charge marginal rates of income tax of anything up to 80%, 90%, or more. Moreover, an increase in the local rate of, say, one half of 1%, may seem rather small to the taxpayer, and yet raise a great deal of money because it is likely to be paid by a large proportion of the population. An increase in the highest marginal rate of national income tax of, say, from 85% to 90%, is likely to be widely publicized in the media, to meet with fierce opposition from some quarters, while, at the same time, raising relatively small amounts of money because relatively few pay tax at this rate.

Increases in taxes are not only unpopular, but they serve to focus public attention on the tax and to mobilize taxpayers' resistance. Here again, fixed property taxes are at a disadvantage, because their lack of buoyancy means that the tax rate has to be increased in inflationary times in order to maintain their yield in real terms.

In sum, property taxes have all sorts of economic and political disadvantages from the revenue raising point of view, whereas a low standard rate income tax has relatively few disadvantages, by comparison with both property taxes and high marginal rates of national income tax. It is no coincidence that the three countries in this study with the fewest local financial problems all levy a low, standard rate income tax, and all raise a large proportion of their income from this source. None of them relies on a land or property tax for more than 5% of their income.

Given these facts and figures, it is interesting that the Committee of Inquiry into Local Government Finance in Britain recommended that a local income tax should be introduced. The evidence of the present study suggests that this would solve a good many of the income-raising problems of local government in Britain. An obvious policy implication of this chapter, therefore, is that a local income tax has a good deal to recommend it as a way of avoiding some financial problems, although it may not solve the worst crises.

NOTES

1. The percentage increases in GDP in the six countries between 1963 and 1974 were as follows: Denmark 3.6%, Italy 3.8%, Norway 3.8%, Sweden 3.1%, UK 2.4%, West Germany 3.6%. These figures are taken from OECD, *National Accounts of OECD Countries*, Vol. 1, *Main Aggregates*, 1974, pp. 58-104.

2. These points are documented in *Report of the Committee of Inquiry into Local Government Finance* (Layfield Committee), Cmnd 6453, London: HMSO, 1976, p. 43.

7

Problems of Inflexibility and Political Sensitivity

Introduction

In many communities budget day is the most exciting, the most controversial, and the most bitterly fought out event in the local authority calendar. This is because local finances are a highly sensitive political issue in these communities with local leaders and citizens, parties and pressure groups taking up committed stands on the question of local taxes and spending. The visibility of local taxes helps to account for their strong emotional and ideological importance, and so does the visibility and unpopularity of the fees and charges which local government makes for some of its services. Political conflict surrounding the budget is further heightened in some countries where there is a legal obligation to balance the budget, and also by the fact that local government can often calculate even very small items of income and expenditure with unusual accuracy. At the same time, a variety of economic and governmental constraints make some sources of local income, notably fees and charges, less adaptable and more inflexible than taxes such as income tax and VAT. Countries, such as Denmark, which raise a relatively small proportion of their local income from highly sensitive sources such as property taxes and fees and charges, appear to benefit from more flexible and low-temperature budgetary politics.

The inflexibility and political sensitivity of local finances

The previous chapter has shown that local authority income in some countries is kept under a tight rein because some of their local taxes are both highly visible and lacking in buoyancy during inflationary periods. However, there are other sources of local income which also contribute to financial problems. The most important of these concerns the fees and charges which local authorities levy on the general public for the services and facilities they provide. This chapter will show, firstly, that fees and charges are a poor source of income, partly because they are constrained by a variety of rules and regulations, and partly because they are often a political issue of great sensitivity.

Fees and charges as a source of income

It is helpful to distinguish between what might be called municipal enterprises, which are expected to more or less cover their costs by charging the public an economic rate for the service, and other local services, the charges for which do not cover costs, and may amount to no more than a small proportion of them. Whereas municipal enterprises are supposed to be more or less economically viable on their own, and charge accordingly, fees and charges are partly determined this way but are also an integral part of the general system of taxes, and considerations of social justice and broader policy objectives enter into decisions about them. It is, of course, impossible to draw a hard and fast distinction between the two. Indeed, the distinction between them is sometimes a matter of fierce political controversy, but municipal enterprises often include electricity, water, and gas, and harbour, bridge, and road tolls, whereas fees and charges are more generally levied on such things as municipal funeral services, car parking, recreational, cultural, and education services, medical services, and planning. While municipal enterprises often make losses which have to be covered by subsidies from the public purse, fees and charges are of special interest to this study because they not only contribute to the local resource squeeze, but they also tend to be contentious political issues.

Because it is difficult to draw a clear distinction between income from municipal enterprises and income from fees and charges, and because accounting practices and definitions vary from one country to another, comparisons between countries should be made with great caution. However, the figures in Table 7.1 suggest that all six countries in this survey derive at least a small proportion of their income from fees and charges, the amount being relatively small in Italy and Denmark, and larger in England and Wales and Norway.

Taken as a whole, municipal enterprises and fees and charges are a rather unsatisfactory way of raising money. In the first place they are sometimes bound by laws and regulations which limit their economic use and flexibility. In some countries it is not possible to transfer money from one service account to another, or to subsidize the losses of one service with the profits of another. In Denmark, to give one instance, local authorities are not formally permitted to transfer money between service headings or to balance out profits and losses on different accounts, although in the last few years these restrictions have been eased, and in Denmark, as in other countries, there is more than one way of drawing up local accounts. In other countries, the central government defines the services for which fees and charges can be imposed, and even decides how much is to be charged. These sorts of controls limit the usefulness of fees and charges as a source of local income.

Table 7.1
Fees and charges as a source of local income

	Percentage of gross local income derived from fees and charges	
Denmark	1950/1	4.2
	1978*	9.7
Italy	1952	4.0
	1971	3.0
Norway	1950/1	21.0
	1975	23.0
Sweden	1950/1	20.5
	1970/1	10.4
*England and Wales***	1962/3	22.7
	1971/2	28.5
West Germany	1950	15.0
	1973	16.8

* Budget figures.
** Miscellaneous income including rents, tolls, fees and interest.

Table 7.2
Fees and charges as a percentage of current revenues in Norway, by service, 1975

Service	*% of current revenue*	
	Urban communes	*Rural communes*
Common expenditure	1	2
Administration	3	4
Schools	1	1
Health	42	39
Social sector	9	10
Church and culture	4	2
Area development and housing	31	21
Various	6	2
Municipal enterprises	92	97

Percentage of expenditure met by fees and charges, England and Wales 1973/4

Rate fund services	%
Education: Further	17
School meals, milk, refreshments	34
Other	3
Personal Social Services:	
Children's homes	16
Homes for the elderly	34
Other	5
Libraries, museums, art galleries	5
Refuse collection	4
Parking	60
Other	7
Total	7
Trading services	%
Passenger transport	82
Cemeteries and crematoria	34
Harbours, ports, piers	87
Markets	52
Slaughterhouses	49
Aerodromes	59
Corporation estates and other	25
Total	53
Housing revenue account	61

Source for English and Welsh figures: *Committee of Inquiry into Local Government Finance,* Cmnd. 6453, HMSO: London, 1975, pp. 133-5.

The second major disadvantage of fees and charges is that they generally raise no more than a small proportion of service costs, although taken together they often raise large sums of money. As the figures for Britain and Norway show (Table 7.2), few services cover as much as half their costs with fees and charges, and most of them cover less than 10%.

The third major disadvantage of fees and charges applies equally to municipal enterprises and concerns the fact that many countries limit public activity, at both national and local levels, to services which, though essential, cannot be provided by the private sector at a profit. For example, some municipalities run loss-making public transport in rural areas which would otherwise be isolated; others provide cheap housing for low income groups which might otherwise be forced to live in sub-standard conditions. Only in a few countries are municipalities allowed into those parts of the economy which are capable of making a profit for private business. A notable exception to this general rule occurs in Norway where local authorities run the cinemas. In general, however, a monopoly in the private sector is likely to produce large profits, whereas a public monopoly is likely to involve financial losses, precisely because loss-making activities are the main ones allowed into the public sector. Even if a public enterprise was able to make a profit, there would probably be strong opposition to it doing so.

In some cases it is either impossible or unwise to charge full market rates for a public service because it is linked to a broader policy. Cities sometimes provide free or cheap car parking on their perimeters, together with a free or cheap bus service to the centre, in an attempt to cut down traffic congestion and pollution. Even where it is possible, in principle, to charge the full price for a service, or even to make a profit, it may be unwise in practice to do so. Many local authorities run crematoria and cemeteries on this basis, for it is thought to be in the best interests of public health to maintain centralized control over burial places, and unwise or impracticable, in some cases, to charge more than fairly minimal rates for this service.

Some fees and charges are also set in accordance with the ability to pay. Once again, social justice, and not economics, determines how much money is raised, the more essential the service is thought to be, the less likely it is to recoup its total costs. This means that the municipalities of many countries have a rough and ready set of means tests which enables them to charge for a service according to number of dependants, size of house, or some such indicator of ability to pay. In many instances this means that the recipient pays only a fraction of the cost of the service. In still other cases, a fee or charge may be levied even though it might be more economical to charge nothing. Dog licences and gun licences sometimes fall into this category; the amount of money they raise may be scarcely worthwhile, but it is the regulation of a potential public nuisance which is the concern, and not a profit or loss calculation.

This list of economic and governmental constraints makes fees and charges less adaptable and more inflexible than most other forms of revenue raising. However, it is the last consideration which is probably most important of all. This is that payment for public services is often such an explosive political issue that it is difficult or impossible to charge market rates, or even to increase prices without provoking strong public protests. If, as is most usually the case, local authorities provide services which are essential or highly necessary for the public good, then to price these services out of the reach of the poorer sections of the community is harmful to both society as a whole, and to the deprived individuals. The dividing line between essential and inessential services is, of course, problematic, and so is the whole question of 'reasonable' charges, but many political groups have strong and clear ideas on these matters. Consequently, the issue of fees and charges is frequently a political battleground. Two examples will illustate the point.

Public transport in Milan, and council rents in England

The municipality of Milan recently took the decision to raise the price of a bus ticket from 100 to 200 lire, and to raise the price of a subway ticket from 150 to 200 lire. Even this doubling of the price of a bus journey meant that public transport was still considerably cheaper than in the majority of Western European cities, but, nevertheless, the whole matter attracted widespread public attention, and eventually became an issue which provoked great anger and bitterness. Socialist representatives resigned from the board responsible, and the trade unions involved split over the issue, one going on strike against the wishes of the other two. There were also public protests of a dramatic kind, with widespread damage to buses, and the destruction of automatic ticket machines. Officials in Milan, and in other cities in Italy, will think long and hard before increasing public transport prices as much as this in the future.

In Britain, the rents which local authorities charge for public housing (known as council housing) have long been an acrimonious and emotional political issue. Some people believe that councils should build and control a large proportion of the housing stock, and should subsidize (heavily, if necessary) housing provided for the poorest and neediest sections of the community. Others believe that housing should not be a social service, that local authorities should reduce the amount of housing under their control, and that the great majority of council house tenants should be charged a more or less economic rent. The issue is further complicated by the fact that many people believe that council tenants do not pay local property taxes, and that their rents should be increased to take account of this. In other words, the issue of council house rents in Britain often provokes the classical political battle between proponents and opponents of the welfare state.

Consequently, rent increases in local authorities have sometimes precipitated lengthy and rancorous political campaigns, involving not just elected representatives and the major parties, but also the full attention of the local media and a range of pressure groups, including trade unions, tenants' associations, residents' associations, and ratepayers' organizations. Public pressure is strong enough in some areas to convince elected representatives on the local council that large rent increases would seriously affect their chance of success in local elections, and, as a result, even those who are not committed to cheap housing may be unwilling to support large rent increases. This is no trivial matter for in England and Wales only a little short of 30% of the housing stock is rented from local authorities, and council house rents totalled almost £900 million in 1975/6.

This brief introduction to the politics of municipal fees and charges is enough to suggest that they are beset by quite severe problems as a source of income — they are sometimes bound by laws which limit their flexibility, they rarely cover more than a rather small proportion of total costs, in a few cases they may even cost more to levy than they raise, and they are sometimes the subject of fierce political controversy which makes it difficult and politically expensive to increase them by more than a modest amount.

If the preceding evidence and argument is enough to show that fees and charges are not without their economic and political problems, then it is not surprising to note that they are a relatively static or declining source of income in Italy, Norway, Sweden, and West Germany. They are of small but increasing importance in Denmark, and of large and increasing importance in England and Wales. Nor is it without significance that both Denmark and Sweden now depend upon fees and charges fór only about 10% of their total income (see Table 7.1). On the other hand, it is also true that Italy is even more favoured in this respect, while Norway does not seem to suffer unduly from currently raising almost a quarter of its income from fees and charges. In other words, the evidence suggests that fees and charges have no more than a secondary importance as a factor contributing to the income side of the local resource squeeze. The presence of a large and expanding income tax is of prime importance in the Scandinavian countries, and is only modified to some extent by fees and charges. At the moment, Denmark and Sweden seem to have the best of both worlds, whereas Norway may suffer to some extent.

West Germany and England and Wales have the double disadvantage of raising much of their income from rather unsatisfactory taxes, and of having to rely to a relatively large extent on fees and charges. While the law requres West German municipal enterprises to cover their costs, this has not always been possible, although some cities manage to cover losses on some services, such as public transport, with profits from others, such as water, gas, and heat. In spite of their efforts, however, German municipalities have not managed to make their enterprises significantly more self sufficient.

However problematic it may be in Germany, the most serious situation involves the Italian *Aziende Municipalizzate* (literally, municipalized firms) which are one of the biggest liabilities in the whole system of local finance in that country. Their task is to provide such major services as electricity, water, gas, and milk, to clean the streets and dispose of waste and refuse, and to provide local public transport. Because of the increased need and demand for these services, the number of municipal firms has increased from 225 in 1965 to 488 in 1975. Over the same period their employees increased from 93,000 to 136,000. In theory, these agencies should operate on a market basis, even to the point of making profits, if possible, but in practice their deficits have soared in recent years — from 121 billion lire in 1970 (5% of total local expenditure) to 840 billion in 1975, and to an estimated 1,100 billion in 1976. This gigantic deficit is due partly to a sharp rise in costs, but also to an equally sharp fall in income from charges. In 1965 the *Aziende Municipalizzate* recovered over 75% of their costs through their income from fees and charges, but by 1976 this has fallen to 50%. To a great extent this was due to determined political resistance to price increases. Before leaving Italy, it should be said that accounting practices mean that the full extent of the problems of the *Aziende Municipalizzate* are not always revealed in the annual statements, and this also underlines the point made earlier that it is difficult to compare countries with different accounting conventions.

As hard pressed authorities search for new ways of solving their financial problems, they are likely to try to increase their fees and charges over a wide range of services and facilities. This, in turn, is likely to increase the importance of fees and charges as a political issue. The first glimmerings of the problem have emerged in Norway where the central governemnt has recently expressed a wish that fees and charges should rise by about 10% per annum, more than double the expected increase from tax revenues. But it is not clear how much the communes, the urban communes in particular, can increase their prices without introducing important questions about social justice and the distribution of resources between citizens and authorities. The Financial Director of Oslo has already raised this question in a document about the future of municipal fees and charges. The same issues are likely to be raised in other countries, if, as seems highly possible, they attempt to recoup a larger and larger proportion of the cost of services by charging the general public for them. In short, fees and charges are likely to become increasingly sensitive political issues in the future.

The details of the balanced budget

Important though opposition is to increases in fees and charges for local government services, it is simply a particular instance of a general characteristic of local government in some countries, namely, that many aspects of local finances attract widespread interest and criticism. The politics of governmental taxing and spending are central to the political systems of most nations in the world, but at the local level they sometimes appear to take on a special significance, attracting widespread public interest, intensive activity on the part of many pressure groups and citizen organizations, a constant flow of information and opinion in the mass media, and heated political debate in council chambers and town halls. As we have seen, proposals to increase local taxes, or the price of local services, have resulted in strikes, resignations, and damage to property. On occasions increases in local taxes or local authority prices have provoked mass demonstrations, rent strikes, public meetings and petitions, and threats that taxes would not be paid.

It is not difficult to see how and why local finances prompt such political passion in some countries. There is, first of all, the tendency for local taxes in some countries to be more visible than central taxes, for all the reasons discussed in the preceding chapter. In general, the more visible the tax, or the more visible the increase in the marginal rate of taxation, the greater its propensity to generate discussion, opposition, and political participation, and the more likely the tax is to become a political issue. Fees and charges share many of the characteristics of visible taxes in that they tend to generate strong feelings of resentment among those who pay them, and a certain amount of opposition — powerful in some cases — to any attempt to increase them. This helps to give visible taxes, and fees and charges, a political importance which is greater than they merit on purely economic grounds.

The tendency for the general public to focus attention on local finances in some countries is reinforced by a series of more technical considerations which give fiscal questions a particular place on the agenda of local decision-making bodies. There is, for example, the general rule that local authorities should balance their budget each and every year. As a result, local officials can — and often do — argue about the smallest details of local budgets, ranging from fractions of a decimal point in tax rates, to small (not to say trivial) items of expenditure. Local officials sometimes involve themselves in the construction of detailed estimates for the coming financial year, amending figures and recalculating costs in their fight for their favourite causes. If it is suggested that such details should be left to professional administrators, it is often argued that local government has a great advantage over central government precisely because the local politician can oversee the finest points of departmental finance and administration. More recently local government has started to budget for a period of years, and these long and medium term plans have also stimulated a great deal of debate.

Central government, in contrast, is not required to balance its annual budget. On the contrary, its role as general manager of the national economy requires it to budget for a surplus or a deficit, as national economic circumstances seem to require. This means that although discussion of central government budgets may be heated, it rarely comes down to the fine detail of local debate. Balancing the budget for a local authority means exactly that, but even fine tuning the economy, so far as central government is concerned, means nothing more than manipulating the budget within fairly large margins of error. If the error grows too large, there is always the possibility of a mid-year budget.

Indeed, central governments could scarcely balance their budgets exactly even if they wanted to. They can calculate neither their income nor their expenditure with any precision, but must rely on fairly approximate estimates over any twelve month period. This is, of course, because national budgets depend upon factors (inflation, international trade, the weather, commodity prices, strikes, political and economic pessimism, changes of government, war) which are not only largely uncontrollable, but also subject to rapid and unexpected change. Some, but not all of these factors affect local budgeting, and to this extent local authorities are able to make more exact financial calculations each year — not with absolute precision, it is true, but with something closer to it than the most skilled of economic forecasters can manage for central governments. Local authorities usually know the size of their government grants to within a few percentage points; they can calculate income from property taxes with little error, and the margin of error in calculating revenues from a local income tax is likely to be smaller for a small population than a large one.

This helps to give the annual budget-setting exercise a special place in the annual cycle of political events, and it gives the discussion of the budget a particularly firm basis. Consequently, clear political positions can be taken, hard evidence can be used for and against any particular proposal, and the costs of any given item can be agreed and discussed in some detail. It is scarcely surprising that finances are prone to loom larger on the local political agenda than almost any other single issue, and that the budget debate is often the longest and most emotional of the political year.

None of this suggests that financial matters are inconsequential in the affairs of central government. To argue this would be plain nonsense. The point being made is that taxing and spending generates relatively more political interest and debate among elected representatives and the general public at the local level, than at the national level. The word 'relative' should be stressed — although local government spends less than central government, it sometimes generates a level of political involvement which is, if anything, out of proportion to the amount of money involved.

This intensity of political concern often generates two sets of pressures, both of which place restrictions on local income: on the one hand, those who pay the most visible of local taxes, especially property taxes, are inclined to resist increases in tax rates; on the other hand, those who pay fees and charges are often resistant to increases in the price of local services. Between them they create powerful public pressures which make it difficult to increase the proportion of income derived from both property taxes and fees and charges. While it is sometimes the more conservative and affluent sections of society which resist property tax increases, it is often the socialist and poorer sections which resist increases in fees and charges.

Important distributional questions are involved in this battleground. Fees and charges are generally (but not always, by any means) regressive, in that a flat rate charge means that the poorer pay a larger proportion of their income, and a still larger proportion if fees and charges are increased. Property taxes also tend to be regressive, but since they are usually based upon the value of property, they tend to be less regressive than fees and charges, so that increases in these taxes usually fall more equitably on the rich and the poor alike. A shift from property taxes to fees and charges, therefore, has a political significance as well as an economic one, and the revolt of the property taxpayers, seen in some countries in the 1970s, may represent part of a more general shift away from proportional or progressive taxes, to a more regressive tax structure involving fees and charges, VAT, and petrol, tobacco, and alcohol duties. From the point of view of local revenue raising, however, the resistance to increases in taxes and increases in fees and charges has the same effect — they both serve to restrict local income.

The public pressures which prevent income from rising as fast as expenditure are, of course, the other side of the coin of the public pressures from exactly the same sources which help to push expenditure up so fast. For, as pointed out in Chapter 2, the local resource squeeze derives, in large part, from the fact that the general public is both an insatiable consumer of services and a hostile payer of taxes, demanding an ever increased quantity and an ever improved quality of service, while resisting attempts to raise more money to pay for these services. The political sensitivity of local finances in some countries is both a cause of and a reflection of this tendency for the general public to blow hot and cold over the issue of local taxing and spending at the same time. And the fact that local government is local, more proximate, more accessible, and perhaps more democratic than higher levels of government, plus the fact that budget-making is a specially tense political matter among local officials, helps to explain why these officials react nervously to both these sets of incompatible and inconsistent pressures.

Yet local finances are not equally sensitive in all countries. In Denmark it is central government taxing and spending which is the more controversial. This is partly because Danish municipalities raise a relatively small proportion of their income from fees and charges, and partly because, as mentioned in the previous chapter, central government's standard and marginal rates of income tax are high — the latter tend to be very high — whereas local government charges a much lower, standard rate which attracts less attention and is thought by some to be fairer. In addition, the local budget in Denmark, as in some other parts of Scandinavia, is more like that of central government in that it is more open ended. This is partly because local surpluses are invested in land and the money market — what might be called communal capitalism. And lastly, unemployment, inflation, the number of working women, and a number of other economic considerations make it difficult for some local authorities in Scandinavia to calculate their revenues from income tax with great precision. Consequently, the local budget in some parts of Scandinavia, especially Denmark, is less precise and less highly controversial than it is in Britain, for example. Danish municipalities benefit considerably from this low temperature budgeting. Although it exaggerates the difference, one might say that expenditure rises to meet income in the former, and falls to meet income in the latter.

Summary and conclusions

Government taxing and spending is a controversial political issue in all nations and at every level of the political system, but there is evidence to suggest that it is a particularly sensitive matter in local politics in some countries. This may be attributed to a combination of considerations, one of the most important being the visibility of some local taxes, as discussed in the previous chapter. The more visible the tax, the greater the amount of public interest, and the more widespread the hostility and resistance to tax increases. In this sense visible taxes are like fees and charges which also generate a fair amount of public interest, and, not unusually, provoke strong, organized resistance when increases are announced. Fees and charges are also beset by other problems, from the revenue raising point of view: their flexibility is sometimes limited by central government laws and regulations which dictate what services can levy fees and charges, and how much these are to be; they rarely cover more than a small proportion of total costs; and, as already stated, they are often the subject of fierce political battles.

Municipal enterprises suffer from some of these problems, but whereas fees and charges of any size tend to be resisted, it is more usually agreed that municipal enterprises should at least try to cover their costs. In addition, the accounts of municipal enterprises are sometimes separate from those of the local authority, and hence they tend to be removed to some extent from the spotlights of the local political arena. Nevertheless, municipal enterprises add to the financial problems of local government, so far as they make losses which have to be covered by the local public purse. It is less usual for them to make profits which can be used to reduce the resource squeeze, for local government is not often allowed to take over services which are capable of making a profit in private hands.

Fees and charges are only of secondary importance as a factor contributing to local financial problems — the ability to raise a large amount of revenue from an income tax is of prime importance, and is only modified by dependence upon fees and charges. However, Denmark and Sweden are at an advantage on both scores since they raise relatively small amounts from fees and charges, and large amounts from their income taxes. Britain and West Germany have the double disadvantage of raising a little or nothing from income taxes, and relatively large amounts from fees and charges. Italian communes raise only a small amount from fees and charges, but they also subsidize, heavily in some cases, the separate accounts of municipal enterprises.

If local authorities try to ease their financial problems by trying to recoup a higher proportion of costs on a wider range of services, as seems entirely likely, then it seems that fees and charges will become a bigger political issue in the coming years. There are already indications of this trend in some places.

Among the other factors which contribute to the politically delicate nature of local finances is the fact that local authorities often have to balance their annual budget by law, and the fact that annual income and expenditure can often be calculated with a high degree of precision. This serves to focus and sharpen local debate and conflict over financial matters. Public finance at the national level is also a highly controversial matter, of course, but national governments are neither required to balance their budgets, nor can they calculate their income or expenditure with any precision. This reduces the political temperature to the extent that decisions are taken with a fairly wide margin of financial error.

However, local finances are not equally sensitive in all countries. In Scandinavia, particularly Denmark, the high standard and marginal rates of income tax levied by central government are highly controversial, while the low, standard rate of the municipalities attracts less attention. In addition, the local budget tends to be rather more open ended than in Britain, for example, because central government grants are not distributed in the same way, and because variables such as inflation and unemployment make it less easy to calculate revenues from income taxes. The Scandinavian countries, and Denmark in particular, benefit from this form of low-temperature budgeting.

8

Urbanization and the Big City Factor

Introduction

This chapter examines the special financial circumstances of urban authorities, especially of big city governments, because they often suffer from a particularly tight resource squeeze. For all the countries for which we have evidence in this study, urban government is more expensive than its rural counterpart, and the larger the city the proportionately more it seems to spend on public services. It cannot be assumed that high levels of expenditure are a sign of high costs, for there is evidence to suggest that big cities set high standards for many public services, and spend accordingly. But there is also good evidence to show that urban government costs more. There are many reasons for this, including the following: the larger and more densely populated the area the more it spends on such things as refuse disposal, street furniture, planning, car parking, public transport, and parks; the diseconomies of scale, although these seem to be of fairly marginal importance; the more important a city is as a regional capital the more it is likely to spend on special services such as large libraries, museums, art galleries, concert halls and theatres, sports centres, and special educational and welfare facilities; the more important a city is as a regional centre, the more commuters and visitors it is likely to attract, and the greater the demands of services such as roads, police, public health, and planning, and lastly, there is a certain amount of evidence from some countries to suggest that the bigger cities have more left wing governments, which tend to spend rather more on such services as housing, education, and social services.

On the income side, it seems that cities in some countries suffer from a central government grants system which favours rural areas, and also from having to raise a relatively large proportion of income from fees and charges.

Not all expenditure is attributable to costs if, by the latter, is meant unavoidable expense which is beyond immediate control. An authority which is bound by law to educate its children will incur the costs of providing school buildings, equipment, and paying teachers' salaries; a nationally negotiated increase in salaries will then increase costs further. But an authority which prides itself on its high quality education is likely to incur extra expenses which are optional and which could, in the last analysis, be cut. In other words, all costs incur expenditure, but not all expenditure is attributable to costs. The purpose of this chapter is to show that urban government, especially the government of large urban places, has a higher expenditure than small or rural government, and that a significant part of this extra expenditure is due to the high costs of urban government.

The costs of urbanization

Most Western European nations are long past their period of rapid urban growth, but even so, statistics (reproduced in Table 8.1) show that the six countries in this study are still urbanizing at a steady pace and that the percentage of the population living in cities of half a million or more is also increasing. In addition, new suburban areas are being created, while other regions are passing through a period of counter-urbanization in which people, industry, and commerce are relocating themselves by moving out of the older and larger urban areas, and into smaller towns and rural regions.

These three processes of urbanization, suburbanization, and counter-urbanization all involve local government in additional expense; new roads and street lighting have to be provided and maintained; sewerage and water supply systems have to be extended; schools have to be built in the expanding areas, and so do community centres, health centres, sports grounds, and the like; new fire and police stations are required, or additional staff taken on at the old ones; new branch libraries may be necessary; more local authority planning activity is required. In short, the movement of people and business to new locations is likely to incur extra expense of one kind or another, not just for the provision of expansive and capital intensive urban infra-structure, but also for its operation and maintenance.

Table 8.1
Urban population and its growth rates

	% urban		*% in cities with a population of 500,000 or more*	
	1950	*1970*	*1950*	*1970*
Denmark	67.3	80.1	27.3	29.8
Italy	44.0	51.5	11.1	17.3
Norway	42.2	54.9	15.4	15.2
Sweden	55.4	66.1	13.2	24.7
UK	77.5	79.1	53.0	54.3
West Germany	72.5	82.2	80.6	84.9

Source: Kingsley Davis, *World Urbanization 1950-1970, Volume I,* Berkeley, Calif.: Institute of International Studies, 1969, Table C.

Paradoxically, the growth and change of the urban system not only involves cities in extra expense, but also rural areas, for they are still obliged to maintain essential services to the same standard. Therefore, declining populations may produce higher per capita costs. Schools in depopulated rural areas are typically a costly item on local budgets. Water and sewerage systems still have to be maintained, even if they have fewer and fewer users. The road network must still be repaired. Social workers may have to travel longer and longer distances to reach their clients. Some costs can be cut as areas lose population, but in the short run it may be difficult to do anything about the amount committed to capital investment, and existing social capital cannot be run down overnight, even if it is under-used.

There appears to be no link between the degree of urbanization and the extent of financial problems in the six nations. Germany, Denmark, and the UK differ only marginally in their high degree of urbanization, although, of course, they have financial problems of different magnitudes. Italy and Norway are the least urban and they also have different financial characteristics. In other words, although urbanization contributes to increasing local expenditure, the degree of urbanization seems to have no close or direct connection with the severity of the resource squeeze.

Urban costs

But probably more important than the costs of urbanization is the tendency for the overall costs of the government and administration of large urban places to be more expensive than that of smaller towns and rural areas. There are many reasons for this. In the first place, some of the services and facilities which can easily be provided privately in rural areas must, almost of necessity, be collectively provided in large and densely populated cities. In theory, it is perfectly feasible for those living in sparsely populated areas to have their own well for water, or cesspool for sewage, a private rubbish dump and a bonfire for refuse, private land for car parking, and fields, woods, and hedgerows for children to play in. City governments, as the nineteenth century reformers discovered, must provide public water, refuse disposal, and sewerage systems. And as the twentieth century has progressed, we have discovered how important it is to plan cities, regulate parking space, and provide play space to keep children off the roads.

It is possible for city dwellers to provide some of these services for themselves, but the greater the population density and the larger the urban area, the more likely they are to create a public nuisance in doing so. For example, a parked car in a suburban side street may create an inconvenient osbtruction for only a few people, but the same car in the central business district might easily create a traffic jam in minutes. Smoke from garden fires may be tolerated in the suburbs, but those in tower blocks obviously cannot burn their rubbish. And although children can and do play on the city streets, the consequences are occasionally dire. A noisy party in the country may not be heard by the nearest neighbours, but in the city it is likely to become yet another chore for police attention. The old saying that no man is an island unto himself has special and costly implications for city government, the more so the bigger and more congested the city.

Cities are also obliged to provide a range of services and amenities which are less necessary in rural areas. Although country roads need their hedges cut and their ditches drained, they do not need pavements, street lights, parking notices, or many traffic signs; their cross roads do not require traffic lights, roundabouts, pedestrian crossings, or under-passes. Rural authorities are also obliged to provide fewer amenities such as public toilets, public parks, and litter bins by the roadside.

Even exactly the same services may cost more in the larger and older urban agglomerations. This is partly because old social capital, installed in the nineteenth century, may be expensive to maintain, more expensive to modernize, and still more expensive to replace. Town halls and administrative buildings opened in 1879 may have been ideally suited to their day, but be inadequate for the demands of 1979 — expensive to heat, costly to maintain, and inefficient into the bargain. And yet to pull down a large building of this kind would undoubtedly disrupt services, both public and private. Similarly, road or bridge repairs in a rural area may affect only a few people, while the same operation in a big city might well cause a major disturbance, requiring traffic re-routing, police, and high labour charges for the night-time and week-end labour necessary to get the job done as quickly as possible.

Large cities may also run up against diseconomies of scale. It is commonly believed that large administrative systems suffer from a certain amount of red-tape, inefficiency, and inertia, just as it is claimed that they are more likely to make mistakes and implement poor policy decisions which, in turn, are likely to be expensive and difficult to change. The truth in these popular beliefs has never been clearly established, but even if it was, they would not necessarily reflect upon the quality big city administrations, or the ability of the public officials who run them. The fact of the matter is that large scale urban-industrial society cannot be run without large scale government and public bureaucracies, and these are necessarily subject to certain limitations. Exactly what the limitations are, and at what point in the growth of public bureaucracies they set in, is not at all clear, for there are both economies and diseconomies of scale and big cities may benefit from the first while suffering from the second since different services have a different optimum population size; a city which is well over the optimum threshold for one service, may be at the optimum for another.

A third possible reason for high service costs in large cities is their tendency to attract a more than proportionate share of the poor, the deviant, and the needy. In this sense big cities often serve as a honey-pot, attracting (or perhaps themselves creating) sections of the population with special housing, social service, or health needs. In the twentieth century, this tendency has been reinforced by the outward movement of middle and upper class people to the suburbs and beyond, leaving the inner city with its special problems. This has not happened in all cities, or in all countries (Central Paris, for example, has established quite the reverse pattern) but in many cases the large cities have the worst social problems, and therefore need special attention from housing, public health, education, and social service agencies.

Moreover, social problems may be more noticeable in urban areas. Rural poverty is often less visible because it is thinly dispersed, and located in far flung places. Rural poverty may also *look* less awful because of its pleasant, pastoral setting. Besides, a problem family in the country is likely to create less of a problem for fewer people, whereas exactly the same family may create a nuisance for a large number of neighbours in a densely populated place. A small collection of such families can create the beginnings of a slum, with demands for public action. In short, social problems are likely to attract more attention in cities, and more pressing demands for public action.

There is still another set of factors which may increase the costs of urban government. Cities which act as 'central places' — that is, as capitals for their surrounding regions — are likely to bear extra costs in providing a range of specialized services and amenities. In the same way that national and regional capitals have a range of specialized shops, entertainment, and commercial facilities, so they are likely to have their own special public services — museums, art galleries, libraries, concert halls, sports centres, parks and gardens, special educational institutions, and so on. Some of these extra expenses may not be costs as defined at the beginning of the chapter, but the case for providng many of these services will be compelling in the largest cities. Central place cities may also bear the burden of catering for large numbers of commuters and visitors who add to the costs of roads, traffic management, and police, and perhaps of public health and refuse disposal as well. The more important the central place, the more it is likely to spend on special public services, and on meeting costs generated by large population flows.

The costs of big city government may also be high precisely because they find it relatively cheap to produce some specialized services. In Norway, for example, it has been calculated that communes with a population of more than 60,000 can buy relatively expensive rubbish disposal systems which sort and re-cycle. Smaller places have to use a cheaper and less satisfactory system because it is economically inefficient for them to use the more expensive method. Similarly, although cities and rural areas require fire services of the same quality, ten fire stations might well suffice in a densely populated area, whereas in a large rural area with the same population size, it might require over a hundred fire stations to provide the same service. In fact it may be so expensive to provide even a rudimentary service in the sparsely populated area that the attempt is not even made. It is partly for this reason that rural areas tend to lack some of the services provided in cities — fire service, water and sewerage, libraries, museums, and many other facilities which require a town or a city of a certain size to make them possible.

Lastly, although rural politics tend to be somewhat conservative, large cities are more likely to be controlled by left wing parties, although there are some notable exceptions to this generalization. There is some evidence from some countries, to show that left wing parties of either a social democratic or communist kind spend more on certain types of services than their more right wing and conservative opponents. They generally spend rather more on redistributive and socially ameliorative services such as housing, education, and social services, although they may also save on other services which do not have the same ideological appeal. Research has shown that the left party effect is not always large, but it is another factor which adds to the expenditure of the larger cities in some countries.

Enough has been said in the brief introduction to this chapter to show the great variety and extraordinary complexity of factors contributing to the expenditure involved in running big cities. To untangle the web of cause and effect, and to show what factor has what sort of impact on urban spending patterns would be a research task of very considerable complexity, requiring expensive and time consuming research. This is obviously well beyond the scope of the present study. Nevertheless, the intricacies of the problem do not prevent a broad view of urban costs in the six countries, and although this chapter is often more tentative and exploratory than the others, it is still possible to draw some conclusions. Given the nature of the data available for most countries, and the exceedingly complex nature of the problem, it seems best to review the state of affairs in each country before returning to some general conclusions.

Denmark: the resource squeeze in the Copenhagen region

As already noted, the degree of urbanization of a country seems to have little or no connection with the severity of its local financial problems, but within any given country it is often noticeable that the largest cities have the worst problems. In Denmark, it is certainly true that two of the largest authorities have the worst resource squeeze. These are Copenhagen and Frederiksberg which, together, make up Greater Copenhagen. They contain 14% of the Danish population and yet they account for almost 28% of local expenditure in Denmark.

Among the causes of this high spending is the rather special age distribution of the Greater Copenhagen population, combined with the fact that several institutions of national importance in the city are run and financed by local government. However, the most important cause of the resource squeeze seems to be the bias of central government grants towards sparsely populated authorities. Because of high densities and also because of the high incomes of residents, the capital region received a relatively small and declining proportion of the total grant; in 1972/3 this stood at 17%, but by 1976/7 it had declined to 11%. During this period, therefore, the Copenhagen region has not only received a small and declining grant in proportion to its expenditure, but the grant has also been small in relation to its population.

This has had two main effects. Firstly, capital expenditure in the region was cut from 20% of the national total in 1972/3, to 14% in 1976/7. Second, in an attempt to maintain the level and quality of local services, local taxes in the capital region have been increased quite considerably. They are now appreciably higher in Copenhagen than in the country as a whole, and they are getting higher. This has angered local residents, and consequently, local taxing and spending has become a widely and hotly debated political issue in the region.

Copenhagen and Frederiksberg seem to represent extreme cases of a general pattern in Denmark in which the larger the municipality the higher its total, net, per capita expenditure is likely to be. As Table 8.2 shows, the largest four municipalities in the country spend almost 25% more than towns with fewer than 10,000 inhabitants, and there is a clear increase in expenditure with each increase in city size.

Table 8.2
Big city, and left party effects in Danish communes, 1972/3

	Municipal inhabitants				
	Less than 10,000	*10,000 to 19,999*	*20,000 to 99,999*	*100,000 or more*	*Total*
Total net expenditure	5,049	5,179	5,353	6,270	5,148
Socialist strength*	32.7%	36.5%	50.3%	59.6%	37.0%
(N)	(161)	(66)	(46)	(4)	(277)

* Percentage voting social democratic, socialist, or communist in local elections, 1970.

Table 8.2 also shows that the bigger the city the greater its socialist strength, and although party politics are commonly believed to have little impact or importance in Danish local government, research on social welfare, primary schools, and roads shows that socialist municipalities do, in fact, spend more on the first two, and less on the last, than other communes. Since roads constitute less than 3% of current expenditure and social welfare and education make up almost 80%, it seems that socialist municipalities are inclined to spend relatively heavily on services which are expensive. It seems, therefore, that a big city factor and a left party effect operate in Denmark, and that both help to explain the tendency for larger cities to spend more on their public services, although not necessarily more on any given service.

At the moment it is impossible to say how the issue will be resolved, but meanwhile it is clear that Greater Copenhagen is in a worse financial situation than other Danish communes, and that this is due to two main factors. Expenditure is high, although the figures will not allow us to pinpoint all the reasons for this, and grants are low. These two factors combine to produce a local resource squeeze which is severe by Danish standards.

Italy: the financial problems of large urban communes

Italian data show that the larger the commune the greater its per capita spending. Table 8.3 picks out figures for small, medium sized, and large communes, and shows that large communes spend the most on their current accounts, on interest charges, on special agencies, and on salaries and wages. More detailed figures for communes of all sizes are too voluminous to produce here, but they also show that the larger the commune the larger its per capita spending.

The clear relationship between urban size and costs in Italian communes is explained by many different factors. First, although Italy is less urban than the other five nations, it is urbanizing at a fast rate. Generally speaking, communes of 20,000 or more are gaining population, while smaller ones are losing. Medium sized communes with between one and five hundred thousand people are growing fastest. This pattern of urban growth helps to explain the relatively heavy investment in schools, roads, and sewerage in Italy.

Second, although there is no systematic evidence about the costs of urban government, or about the economies and diseconomies of scale, one detailed study shows that population size and urban congestion contribute towards the costs of government in large cities. In his research on local spending in the Turin metropolitan region, Gianni Zandano found that high expenditures were related to factors such as population size and density, and degree of urbanization. He suggests that this may be caused either by the diseconomies of scale, or by the demand for more and better services in large cities.[1] Confirming the latter interpretation is the fact that the larger Italian cities generally have more economically inactive people (including students, retired people, and housewives), many of whom require public services of one kind or another. There is, therefore, reason to believe that the larger cities produce services for a larger proportion of the population than smaller places.

Table 8.3 also shows that municipal enterprises in the largest cities run large deficits. It is not possible to do more than speculate about the reasons for this, but it seems plausible to suggest that the larger cities will not only have more enterprises but will also deliver their services to a larger proportion of the population — almost every household in a large city will have access to water, gas, electricity, and public transport, which is not necessarily the case in rural areas. In addition, it is possible that political resistance to increased charges for these services is better organized and more powerful in the cities. Consequently, deficits are likely to be larger and to involve large scale services.

Table 8.3
Expenditure of Italian communes on selected items, by population size

Population size	*Per capita current expenditure (lire)*	*% interest on current account*	*% deficit on current account of special agencies**	*Employees per thousand population*	*Ratio of salaries to consumption expenditure*
1-5,000	23,000	9.0	0.0	5.3	1.31
20,000-30,000-	29,430	13.6	0.4	5.8	1.40
More than 50,000	80,360	24.0	10.4	11.3	1.80

* Mainly gas, water, electricity and transport.

Source: P. Giarda, *La Struttura delle spese degli enti locali,* Luglio: Dipartmento di economia politica, Universita degli studi delle Calabria, Doc. di ricerca n.7, Arcavate di Rende, 1974,

And lastly, the latest research shows that Italian cities which are controlled by left parties and coalitions tend to spend more on public services than those with centre or right wing governments. Though the research results are still tentative, they indicate that left wing cities generally spend rather less on their capital accounts, but more on the current side, particularly on education, housing, and social services. Party control, however, cannot wholly explain the fact that big cities in Italy are the biggest spenders, simply because until 1975, the biggest cities were usually controlled by the Christian Democrats or by centre-right coalitions, who did not show any high spending tendencies. It was not until the large swing to the left in the elections of 1975 that the communists and socialists took over the largest cities, and although it is still very early days, an examination of 1976 budgets indicates that left governments have a tendency to increase current expenditure in these cities, while cutting capital investment.[2] In other words, the Italian evidence shows that there is a 'big city factor' which creates high costs for big city governments, as well as a 'left party factor', and that these two may well combine in the larger cities to create levels of spending that are higher than the average. It must also be said that these are rather cautious conclusions which await confirmation from more detailed studies covering a longer period of time.

Norway: urban-rural differences and the big city factor

Norwegian figures show that local services are more expensive in urban than in rural areas. Capital expenditure is over 40% higher, and current spending over 60% higher, these differences being due mainly (as Table 8.5 shows) to higher per capita spending on wages and salaries, social and welfare services, public works, and streets and roads. Only in the case of current and capital spending on schools does spending in rural areas exceed that of the urban areas. This partly reflects the high costs of running village schools in rural areas, but it is also due to the capital costs of a large school building programme in rural communes. In fact, the latter have increased their total capital and current expenditure at a fast rate in the past thirty to forty years (see Table 8.4), and are catching up with urban areas in their attempt to improve their level and quality of service provision. Nevertheless, the urban communes continue to spend considerably more than the rural ones at present.

Table 8.4
Per capita current and capital spending in urban and rural communes in Norway, constant prices (1966 = 100)

	Rural communes		*Urban communes*	
Capital expenditure	*1950*	*1971*	*1950*	*1971*
Per capita	228.5	634.1	494.7	909.1
Index	100	277	100	184
Current expenditure	*1950*	*1974*	*1950*	*1974*
Per capita	323.2	1,179.5	999.8	1,892.7
Index	100	365	100	189

Table 8.5
Per capita expenditures in Norwegian Kroner on selected services in urban and rural communes

	Rural communes		*Urban communes*	
Current expenditure				
Wages and salaries	1971:	1,052	1975:	1,512
Social services*		233		239
Welfare contributions		61		181
Schools		693		556
Public works		114	1971:	238
Capital expenditure				
Schools		199		125
Streets and roads		84		160
Other public works		128		155

* Not including contributions.

Although services are probably more costly in Norway's urban communes, it is also evident that the lion's share of central government grants is channelled to the rural areas, on the grounds that they need the money to raise the level of their sevices. The towns and cities, therefore, have had to rely more on local taxes, and especially on income raised from fees and charges (see Table 8.6). Urban communes raised almost twice as much of their total income from fees and charges as rural communes in 1971. As we have already seen in the previous chapter, local politics makes it difficult to increase fees and charges for public services, so that city finances have suffered accordingly.

Table 8.6
Percentage distribution of municipal revenues in urban and rural communes in Norway, 1962 and 1971

	Rural communes		*Urban communes*	
	1962	*1971*	*1962*	*1971*
Local taxes	61.6	53.3	57.1	54.4
Government grants	17.0	22.1	6.5	11.9
Fees and charges	15.7	14.4	32.1	28.2
Other	5.7	10.0	4.3	5.6
Total income	100.0	99.8	100.0	100.1

Table 8.7
Per capita municipal debts in urban and rural communes in Norwegian Kroner, at constant prices (1966 = 100)

Rural communes		*Urban communes*	
1950	*1974*	*1950*	*1974*
111.2	1,399.2	1,119,9	2,351.0

High service costs combined with relatively restricted incomes have caused urban communes in Norway to build up high per capita debts. Table 8.7 shows that indebtedness was 70% greater in urban than in rural communes in 1974. Once again, the very rapid increase in rural spending has caused debts to mount up quickly (they increased more than twelve times between 1950 and 1974) but, nevertheless, urban communes still outstrip rural ones in this respect.

This indicates that urban areas have a tighter resource squeeze than rural ones, and it also seems that this state of affairs is repeated in a magnified form in the very largest cities. There are three cities in Norway with a population of one hundred thousand or more (Oslo, Bergen, and Trondheim), and throughout most of the post-war period their per capita current and capital spending has been considerably higher than other urban areas — particularly current spending on welfare, and on wages and salaries, and capital spending on education and public works. Moreover, their rate of increase in spending is higher than in other urban authorities.

Table 8.8
Expenditures in communes of different sizes, in Norwegian Kroner, at constant prices (1966 = 100)

		Population size		
		Less than 10,000	*More than 100,000*	*All urban communes*
Per capita current expenditure	1962	1,295	1,441	1,371
	1975	1,836	3,079	2,366
Per capita capital expenditure	1962	676	774	762
	1971	949	1,173	909

At the same time, while the three major cities have large local tax revenues, these are not in proportion to their high rate of spending. And, in addition, they receive relatively small central government grants (337 Norwegian Kroner per capita in 1975 compared with an average of 381 in all urban communes), while raising a higher proportion of their income from fees and charges (1,527 Norwegian Kroner per capita in 1975 compared with an urban average of 1,085). This means that the largest cities have increased their spending more rapidly, and their income more slowly than other authorities (either urban or rural), and as a result they not only have the most adverse Resource Squeeze Ratio, but a ratio which has worsened steadily since 1966. Consequently, the financial situation of the largest Norwegian cities has become a cause for some concern.

Sweden: the costs of indivisible public services in urban areas

In Sweden, as in Norway, per capita spending is generally highest in the largest cities. In 1974 total per capita spending in the largest twenty-one cities was 8,500 Swedish Kroner compared with a municipal average of 6,600. This means that the largest cities spend almost 30% more per resident than the average Swedish municipality. Sweden and Norway are also alike in that their largest cities are increasing their spending at a faster rate than other authorities. Between 1950 and 1967 the growth rate for the largest Swedish cities was 12.2%, which compared with a figure of 11.5% for rural authorities, and 12.0% for all authorities. The largest cities spend particularly heavily on public utilities and enterprises, public health, and on debt interest, but relatively less on education and culture, social welfare, and general administration.

A second look at this list of services will show that the largest cities in Sweden generally spend relatively heavily on indivisible services — that is, on services which are provided for the community as a whole, such as planning and financial administration — and relatively lightly on divisible services — that is on services, such as education, housing, and family welfare, which are directed to particular social groups or individuals. This supports the idea, presented in the introduction to this chapter, that urban life, particularly in large urban areas, generates a need for a wide range of indivisible goods and services which are less pressing in rural areas.

The evidence also suggests that the larger municipalities in Sweden provide more services over a wider range of activities. For example, all municipalities with a population of 50,000 or more have information departments, but none with populations of 20,000 or less can emulate them. The larger cities also have more ice-rinks, more spacious community centres, more school

Table 8.9
Service quality and costs in Swedish municipalities of different size, 1970 (selected indicators)

	Population size			
	Less than 10,000	*10,000 19,999*	*20,000 49,999*	*50,000 or more*
% with information centres	0	0	8	100
Sports grounds per thousand	.3	.2	.3	.2
Heated outdoor swimming pools, per thousand	.02	.004	.01	.01
Indoor ice rinks per thousand	0	.004	.01	.005
Square inches of community centres per thousand	5	28	20	55
Net expenditure per cap. on sports and leisure	18	41	53	56
Financial support to private organizations:				
Instructors	2	2	2	4
Sports	5	9	7	6
Religion	1	.30	.50	.50
Social welfare	1	1	2	5
Education/culture	6	6	7	27
Net per capita support	16	24	23	44
Education				
% with free school breakfast (secondary)	89	100	90	100
% with free school lunch (primary)	23	9	25	75
% with school psychologists	38	45	91	100
Library books per capita	2.9	2.4	2.8	3.4
Social welfare:				
Children in nurseries per 100 aged 0-6	1.2	1.4	2.7	4.5
Children in family nurseries per 100 aged 0-6	2.4	4.7	4.6	8.5
Children in pre-schools per 100 aged 0-6	2.7	6.0	5.7	6.3
Social workers per thousand	.6	.7	.9	1.3

psychologists and library books, better social welfare facilities and more social workers. They also spend more on sports and leisure, and give more financial support to private organizations, especially those concerned with social welfare and education (see Table 8.9). This is good evidence that large cities either provide more and better services, or spend more money in the attempt to do so, or have greater needs and/or demands for services.

While this helps to explain the high expenditure of large Swedish cities, it is also significant that these cities have income problems. In the first place, while the average Swedish municipality derived more than 28% of its total revenue from central government grants, the equivalent figure for the largest cities was some 10% lower. As in Denmark and Norway the rural areas seem to benefit from proportionately larger government grants. This means that Swedish cities must rely more heavily upon taxes, fees, and charges, especially upon the latter, for not only did the big cities raise 48% of their income from fees and charges in 1975, but this was more than two and a half times as much as the average municipality. The big city figure is increasing as fast as it is falling in the country as a whole.

There is no noticeable left party effect in Sweden. The big cities are not more likely to be controlled by left parties, and nor are left parties at the local level more likely to spend on public services, although there is some evidence to suggest that they affect the pattern of expenditure to a small extent. Norway and Sweden are alike in this respect. In brief, the left party effect is not present in Sweden, but the big city effect is, and while the largest cities spend more, they also get less in grants and have to rely upon fees and charges to a greater extent than smaller towns and cities.

Britain: cities and counties, and the big city factor

The government of predominantly urban areas in Britain costs more than that of rural areas. In 1972/3 the county boroughs (which included all the largest cities and some smaller ones) spent £96.4 per capita, while the counties (which were predominantly but not exclusively rural) spent £83.5. The cities spent more on police, welfare, personal and public health, fire, libraries, and planning, while the counties spent more on education and highways.

In general the most rural and sparsely populated areas spent least on sewage and refuse disposal, and on police, fire, planning, public health, and street lighting, reflecting, perhaps, the fact that these services are not as absolutely essential in rural as in urban places, and also the fact that it would be prohibitively expensive to provide them to a high standard in such places. Among the more important services, however, education stands out as being relatively expensive in rural areas, presumably because all children must be educated, and because small village schools are notoriously expensive.

There is also some evidence to show that the Labour Party, which generally controls a higher proportion of cities than counties, spends relatively heavily on some local government services, particularly on some of the more expensive ones such as education, housing, health, and social services. In part, this is due to the fact that the largest cities often have the most pressing needs for these services, but there also seems to be a tendency, which is significant but not particularly strong, for Labour controlled authorities to spend more on socially ameliorative and redistributive services.

The cities which spend the most on public services, however, are the largest and most important of the regional capitals. Outside London (which spends particularly heavily), the highest service costs are borne by the five largest regional capitals, which spend more per resident on nine of the fourteen public services provided by city governments. In addition, cities which are second only to the major metropolitan capitals in the largest urban agglomerations in the country, also spend more (in total and on ten out of fourteen services) than the national average.

Diseconomies of scale may help to explain part of these high service costs, but they cannot explain all of them. For example, although library expenditure correlates with size, it correlates more strongly with the importance of the city in the national urban hierarchy. It seems that major urban centres spend more partly because they provide large and specialized libraries which are used by those who live in the big cities, and by those in the surrounding urban and rural hinterland. The same appears to be true of spending on parks, leisure and sports facilities, and special education. And because huge numbers of people visit the big cities for business and pleasure purposes, these cities also bear extra costs for such services as police, planning, and highways.

Table 8.10
Service expenditures of the largest cities in England and Wales

Per capita expenditures (£) on:	*Metropolitan capitals* (5)	*Secondary capitals* (6)	*County borough average* (83)
Education	15.31	15.34	15.31
Libraries	.67	.51	.50
Sewerage	.62	.98	.86
Refuse	1.05	.81	.78
Parks	.97	.93	.85
Public health	.50	.44	.45
Personal health	1.53	1.53	1.42
Children	.61	.54	.49
Welfare	.60	.75	.71
Housing	2.13	1.71	1.85
Planning	.13	.11	.17
Highways	2.55	2.34	2.25
Fire	.61	.55	.64
Police	2.80	2.47	2.26
Total expenditure	31.45	30.21	29.71

Notes: 1. Metropolitan capitals are Manchester, Birmingham, Liverpool, Leeds, Newcastle.

2. Secondary capitals are Bolton, Bradford, Croydon, Huddersfield, Salford, Wolverhampton.

3. The figures are for the financial year 1960/1.

Conclusions

This review of the expenditure of urban government has had to be brief, partly because rather little is known about certain aspects of the subject, and partly because it has been necessary to condense what is known into one short and inadequate chapter. The subject seems to be of such importance, though, that it merits much closer and more detailed inspection in the future. At the same time, it is possible to draw some general conclusions from this chapter which will help our understanding of the financial circumstances of urban areas in Western Europe.

The chapter starts off by pointing out that it should not be assumed that higher expenditure on the part of large cities necessarily means higher costs, if by the latter is meant unavoidable expenses. Higher expenditure may be voluntarily incurred by city officials because, for whatever reason, they want the city to have more or better services than other areas. The evidence in this chapter suggests that part of the higher expenditure of cities can be explained in this way, and that another part can be explained in terms of the higher costs of urban government.

It is clear that urban government is generally more expensive than rural government in Denmark, Italy, Norway, Sweden and the UK. This seems to be due to the fact that urban areas often have to spend on a range of public services and facilities such as refuse disposal, street lighting, planning and parking provision, parks and public works. While rural areas may need these services to some extent, it seems that the need is often less pressing. On the other hand, rural children need an education no less than city children, and since rural schools are often relatively expensive to run, per capita costs in rural places are usually rather high. In general, though, it is the cities which outspend the rural authorities, and frequently by quite a large margin.

In the second place, the larger the city, the more it is likely to spend on public services. This is due to what may be called the big city factor which, in its turn, breaks down to a variety of different causes. There are most probably some diseconomies of scale in large cities which will account for a certain proportion of the extra costs. But popular though this explanation is, it is not the only important aspect of big city finance, and it may well not even be among the most important factors. In addition to the diseconomies of scale there is also the fact that the larger the city the more likely it is to produce a range of highly specialized (and often expensive) public services, not only for its own residents but also for those who live in the surrounding area. Big city facilities are likely to include special sports and recreational centres (theatres, art galleries, museums, libraries, concert and opera halls, parks and zoos, athletics tracks, swimming pools, skating rinks) as well as special educational institutions for gifted children, for the arts, and for higher education and research. While city governments rarely underwrite the total cost of these services, they are likely to provide some of them, and subsidize a good proportion of the others. In any case, they also have to provide services for those who visit the city for its special facilities, and hence spend quite large amounts on such things as highways and police. There is also good evidence to show that Swedish cities provide more and/or better services than the smaller towns.

And lastly, there is some evidence of a left party effect which complements the big city effect in Denmark, Italy, West Germany and the UK although not in Norway or Sweden. There are many methodological difficulties with this research, and hence caution prevents drawing any firm conclusions, but it does seem that the larger cities in these four countries tend to be controlled by left wing parties, and that these parties spend more on some services (such as education, social services and housing) and more in total, then conservative and right wing local parties. However, the left party effect is not generally strong, and in Italy it has only operated since 1975 when the Communist Party gained control of some of the largest cities. Nevertheless, the left party effect adds to our understanding of the higher expenditure of big cities in four of the six nations.

The consequences are fairly dire for our cities. Not only are they under pressure to produce more services over a wider range of activities, but they sometimes receive a less than proportionate share of central government grants and depend upon rather unpopular fees and charges for a larger proportion of their income. As a result they are often caught in a tighter resource squeeze than their rural counterparts even though the latter may be increasing their expenditure at a faster rate. In other words, cities are the leading edge of the local resource squeeze in that they display, in a magnified form, most of the symptoms of financial constraint which affect the larger systems of local government.

NOTES

1. Gianni Zandano, *Saggi sulla spesa pubblica locale*, Milan: Giuffre, 1975, pp. 3-42.

2. The latest work has been done by G. Martinotti, who also summarizes the results of previous research — see G. Martinotti, 'Local Financial Problems in Italy', paper delivered to the 9th World Congress of Sociology, Uppsala, Sweden, 14-19 August, 1978, pp. 65-86.

9

How to Balance the Books?

Introduction

The room for financial manoeuvre on the part of local government when it tries to adapt to increasingly tight financial circumstances is limited. The constraints to which it is subject are of four main kinds, namely: social and demographic trends and pressures in society at large; economic and financial pressures created by the nature of its activities and the institutional structure within which it works; government laws and regulations which largely determine what local government does, and how it should finance these activities; and political pressures which mainly derive from the revolution of rising expectations. These constraints leave room for eight different types of response to the resource squeeze, these being: reducing expenditure; transferring services to a higher level of government; transferring services to the private sector; raising more money from fees and charges; expansion into profit making activities; a larger share of better taxes; larger central government grants; and going into debt. Of these, giving local government a larger share of better taxes, especially income tax, has a lot to recommend it, but some central governments are likely to block this solution. Lastly, the chapter draws attention to the special problem of large cities and metropolitan areas, to the crucial role of central government in creating local financial problems, and to the Cinderella status of local government.

Scarcity and the local resource squeeze

It may not be particularly difficult to balance the local government books in the limited and technical sense of making expenditure equal to income so that the deficit before loan transactions is close to zero. In some places this may be quite easy in any given year, although a more difficult and not necessarily sensible thing to accomplish over a longer period of time. But even where the task presents no special or insuperable difficulties, its achievement invariably covers up a set of underlying political, social, and economic tensions which are created by the simple fact that the overall demand for goods and services invariably exceeds their supply. Throughout their recorded history Western societies have been characterized by a strong and compulsive desire on the part of their members to have more than they can conceivably get. To the extent that individuals usually desire more than they have, and are constantly striving to improve the quality of their material lives, there will always be a scarcity of resources, whether of money, space, leisure time, clean air, or accessibility to the attractions of the city and the delights of the countryside at one and the same time.

Although the scarcity problem applies to almost all individuals and organizations in Western societies, it seems to be an especially acute one for the public sector which is not subject to the same set of market forces which adjust supply and demand in the private sector. In the private sector the effective demand for market commodities is held in check by the fact that effective demand, by definition, means the demand for goods and services which the general public is both willing and able to pay for. In the public sector, however, people are often not required to pay for services directly, if they pay for them at all, but rather pay for them indirectly through taxes. This means that some people and groups can consume goods and services at the expense, wholly or partially, of other people or groups. Indeed, much of the domestic politics of the modern state boils down to nothing more complicated than the question of which groups, organizations, or sections of society can consume public services at the expense of others. The problem is complicated by the fact that many people seem to be firmly convinced that they are paying through the nose for the benefits of others who neither deserve nor need half of what they get. Consequently, the political strategy of many groups and individuals is to try to increase their consumption of public goods while cutting tax payments.

The problem of insatiable consumers and hostile taxpayers pervades the whole of the public sector, but as the previous chapters have shown, it is specially acute for local government in those countries where both demands for and expenditure upon public services have risen steeply, and where quite severe limits are placed upon increases in local authority income. Hence the widening gap, in some nations, between local income and expenditure, and hence the increasingly severe nature of the resource squeeze. And yet, as we have seen, the problem is not equally severe in all countries, and in some, notably the three Scandinavian nations in the survey, it is not particularly acute. What can we learn from them? How have they managed to organize local government and its finances so as to avoid a debilitating resource squeeze? More generally, what reforms, changes, innovations, or improvement can be introduced into the system of local government in order to reduce the severity of financial problems. In short, what, if anything, can local government do to improve its financial situation?

It must be recognised at the outset that the room for manoeuvre is limited. While it might be too much to describe local government as a prisoner of its environment, it is nevertheless true to say that its ability to influence, change, or otherwise manipulate its financial circumstances is limited by comparison with business in the private sector, and other levels of government in the public sector. The limitations which act upon it are of four main kinds: social and demographic; economic and financial; governmental; and political. It is worth considering these four sets of constraints, in order to show what local government cannot do, before turning more positively towards what it can and might do.

Economic and financial constraints

No matter how slight the influence of central government over its own domestic economy, and no matter how little influence it may exercise over international economic trends, the power of local government over its economic circumstances is generally less. Local government cannot, for example, print its own money or regulate the money supply, and nor can it exercise much direct influence over the rate of inflation or the minimum lending rate. In some countries, local government must balance its annual budget, and although there are ways of disguising fairly minor deviations from this rule, it means that local authorities cannot build up surpluses in good years to spend in bad ones, just as it means that there are fewer opportunities to finance capital projects from surplus current income. At the same time, local government is sometimes limited in the amount that it may borrow and in the places it may borrow from, in order to finance capital investment. This may have the advantage of central government lending at lower than normal rates of interest, but it may also mean limited flexibility in how much capital is raised and what it is raised for.

Local government costs are also more directly and more immediately affected by inflation than central government costs. This is because it spends proportionately more on wages and salaries which tend to rise faster than other costs during inflationary periods. In addition, inflation pushes up interest rates, thereby increasing the burden of debt payments. In many countries a high proportion of total interest is paid to central government, and one thus has the situation where central government may reprimand local government for increases in expenditure while, at the same time, receiving high interest payments on the money which it obliges local authorities to borrow.

Local government is not an entirely innocent and powerless agent in these respects. It forms a powerful pressure group in its own right, and it also has better access to central government than many, even most, private organizations. On the whole, however, it is central government which is likely to use local government in its attempts to regulate the national and international economy, and it is local government which is under pressure to adjust and accommodate to the economic plans of higher levels of government. Local government can and does try to influence central government in these matters, but it is difficult to believe that it can turn the tables and use central government for its own local purposes.

Local government is also an integral part of broad national and international trends, which few governments at any level have the power to slow down, or reverse, but which have considerable implications for the range and depth of services provided by the public sector. Perhaps the most profound of these is the tendency which is marked in almost all industrial societies for the service sector to expand relative to industry and agriculture. Local government is an important part of this trend since most of its activity is concerned with such services as education, social welfare, police, fire, health, planning, environmental control, and arts and leisure activities. To the extent that modern society is moving towards a more service intensive economy, then local government is likely to expand its range of activities. As such it is the creation, rather than the creator of economic pressures.

The expansion of local services is reinforced by the tendency, noted in an earlier chapter, for increasing affluence to be accompanied by increasing public expenditure. While many people believe that rising public and private expenditure are incompatible, the reverse seems to be the case. A few examples drawn from local services will illustrate the point. The more cars people buy, and the longer the distances they travel in them, the more highways are likely to cost. The more industry requires intelligent and highly trained workers, the greater the demand for education. At the same time the higher the economic and occupational aspirations of the population, the more likely children are to stay at school, and to go on to further and higher education. And lastly, the more leisure time people can afford, the greater the pressure on local authorities to provide parks, museums, libraries, concert halls, theatres, and an ever increasing range of sporting facilities. In this sense, the public sector, and especially the local public sector which is heavily concerned with services, is caught up in an underlying social and economic dynamic of great force. The higher the standard of living in any society, the greater its demands are likely to be for services in general, and local government services in particular. It is ironical, therefore, that the more right wing elements in modern politics who are concerned to increase the size and scope of the private sector, should be so strongly opposed to the growth of the public sector.

Local government has certainly played an active part in creating this state of affairs. It has responded to popular demands and pressures, even helped to create them by promising more and more at each successive election, and both politicians and officials alike have sought to make their political and administrative names by masterminding all sorts of ambitious schemes and projects, and by creating all sorts of wonderful and expensive empires. In other cases, service expansion may have been prompted by a deep professional ethic, or by genuine altruistic motives. Authorities have even been competing with one another in their attempts to produce the best education results, the biggest library, or the best housing record. All of this is indeed true, and it has helped to lift local spending to unprecedented heights, but at the same time, local government forms only a small part of the total complex of social, economic, and political forces which have an effect on virtually every Western society, and which have moulded the development of service provision in both the public and the private sectors.

Social and demographic pressures

If local authorities are bound by law, or caught up by convention, or by popular expectation to provide services and facilities for a given section of soceity, then an increase in numbers of that section is bound to have consequences for the service. Either the authorities concerned can expand their services to keep pace with numbers, in which case they are likely (if they do not benefit from economies of scale) to increase their costs, or else they can spread their services more thinly, keeping costs down. The second strategy may have its own social and political costs, however, in that it might result in more juvenile delinquency, or more road deaths, or a higher infant mortality rate, or else it may provoke a political campaign on the part of parties or pressure groups.

In many cases, however, local government is not permitted the luxury of deciding between these two courses of action, since it may be bound by very carefully specified laws to provide services of a given quality for particular sections of the population. In the post-war period, successive central governments in most Western nations have laid down an enormously wide range of detailed specifications which lay out exactly how services are to be provided and to whom. Thus the raising of the minimum school leaving age has most usually required local authorities to carry a part, if not a large part, of the cost of educating a larger school age population. Similarly, an increase in the number of old people has generally had significant consequences for the cost of welfare services. At the other end of the life cycle, the more mothers of young children go out to work, the greater the demand for day-care centres, most of which are regulated and controlled by local authorities, and many of which are actually run and financed by them. In these cases, local government is the subject of legal and social pressures over which it has no direct control. It may have indirect influence, even considerable indirect influence, over central government regulations and requirements, but it cannot be held responsible for working mothers or the increasing life expectation of the older generation.

There is a further range of demographic trends which have a bearing on the local political economy. First, there is the much discussed movement of middle class individuals to the suburbs and the small towns — the process of suburbanization and counter-urbanization, which may have reached its peak before the oil crisis of 1973. Hand in hand with the relocation of population has gone the relocation of industry, or at least some sections of the more profitable, light engineering, and high technology sections of it, which has a tendency to move closer to its major markets in the so-called golden triangle of the Common Market, which includes the area roughly bounded by Birmingham, Rome, and Hamburg. This has had two effects so far as the local political economy is concerned: it has reduced the size of the tax base in some of the large cities, leaving them, and especially the inner-city cores, with worsened social problems and less money to deal with them; and it has created a need for capital intensive infra-structure in the expanding suburbs and the small towns. Local authorities in some countries may have unintentionally assisted in creating these problems, but the relocation of people and industry is too widespread among countries with a wide variety of local and central government policies to be attributed to these policies alone.

The third demographic trend is the arrival of large numbers of immigrant and guest workers in many European countries. In many cases they make fewer demands upon public services than the native population, but they have tended to highlight already existing problems in housing, welfare, and education, and have also generated a few problems of their own. Some of these fall within the ambit of local government and thus constitute an extra responsibility and an extra expense. The presence of immigrant and guest workers is not, of course, attributable to local government policies, but rather to national governments which have sometimes recruited them to fill gaps in the labour market, and to international organizations, most notably the Common Market, in order to stimulate labour mobility. Once again, local government in many parts of Europe is faced with problems and needs which it was not instrumental in creating.

Government laws and regulations

In most Western societies local government has a range of optional activities which it may choose to engage in, but it also has an immensely long list of services and facilities which it is bound to provide by the force of the law. Since 1945, higher levels of government have removed some items from this list, including some of the more expensive ones, but it has invariably added others. The general tendency has been for state and central government to delegate more and more functions to the municipalities, to specify in ever greater detail the exact quality and quantity of services, and to set ever higher and more expensive minimum standards. In addition, central government in many countries has made a big attempt to raise the service standards of what might be termed the more backward authorities. In short, the range and quality of many of the services and facilities provided by local government is determined in large part not by local authorities themselves, but by higher levels of government, particularly at the national level.

At the same time, the higher levels also have considerable, or even total power over the ways in which local authorities raise their revenues. The latter can often, but not always, set their rate of taxation, but they cannot unilaterally introduce new taxes, or choose to start taxing groups, institutions, or types of wealth, property, or income which are exempted by national law. In effect, therefore, local government does not control either its own range of functions, or the taxes it can employ to finance these functions.

Central government also has a tendency to preserve the best taxes for its own use. The Scandinavian countries in this survey are an exception, but in many other nations the lion's share of the most inflation-proof and the least visible taxes pours into the national exchequer. The localities are not infrequently left with the less appetising crumbs from the taxman's table. The least nutritious of these, from the revenue raising point of view, is the fixed property tax which contributes quite a large proportion of locally derived revenues in many countries in Western Europe, and which is the only tax available to local government in the UK. The lack of a fully adequate set of local taxes makes local government increasingly dependent upon central government grants which, as a result, have been increasing as a proportion of total local income in recent decades. This further erodes the ability of local government to solve its own financial problems, and places it still more at the mercy of forces over which it has no direct control. Whatever the financial and governmental merits of increasing central government transfers, the fact remains that many local officials and politicians are made increasingly uneasy by the fact that they make it more and more difficult for localities to arrange their own financial affairs. At best local government is an equal partner of central government, but more usually it is the Cinderella of the system, taking whatever national government sees fit to hand out.

After taxes and grants, fees and charges form a large part of local income, but these, too, are often bound about by all manner of government rules and regulations which determine who can be charged what sort of fee for what type of service. Whatever the social and political merits of placing constraints on charges for public services, this testifies, once again, to the fact that local government rarely controls its own affairs, but runs them either partly or largely in accordance with the requirements of higher levels of government.

In order to avoid some of these limitations, and also to ease their financial situation, local authorities in many parts of Western Europe have resorted to borrowing, using both short term and long term money markets, and using both private and public sources. Once again, central government often tries to regulate the amount of local authority borrowing, and the sources of the loans. In some cases central government has gone no further than issue a stern warning about the need to limit borrowing to acceptable levels (i.e. a level acceptable to central government), but in other cases it has introduced a fully-fledged set of statutes which determine how much the localities may borrow, from whom, and for what purposes.

Political constraints

The last, and in many ways the least easily defined and measured set of constraints, concerns the political pressures to which local government is often subjected. Political forces of the kind discussed here are broad, general, and fairly intangible, but they seem to be influential nonetheless. By and large they can be brought together under the umbrella concept of 'the revolution of rising expectations', a term which started life to explain recent developments in the Third World, but which is equally applicable to contemporary European society. Like the Third World, Europe has experienced enormous economic growth in the form of the economic miracle which has transformed most of her nations to a greater or lesser extent, and which has produced a quantum jump in people's expectations of life. The revolution has had a full impact upon both private business and public authorities, and within the public sector there is reason to believe that the influence that it has exercised over local government may have been particularly strong.

This partly because the booming activity of local and community pressure groups in the 1960s and 1970s — the much discussed community participation movement — puts local government under increasing pressure to respond to organized citizen demands. It is partly because local government is the obvious target for group pressure simply because it handles the bulk of such services as housing, education, welfare, and planning and environmental control, which are the issue areas around which many community groups organize themselves. And it is partly because local government is, after all, the local, grass-roots level of the political system, and is more responsive to public pressure than higher levels of government. In other words, local government tends to generate a greater sense of civic competence on the part of the general public, a sense which has some basis in reality in that it does actually respond, not to all pressures from all quarters, but at least to many pressures from many sections of society.

This has placed local government in a vulnerable position in that it has had to try to accommodate two sets of opposing political demands — demands for improved service quality and quantity, and demands for lower taxes, fees, and charges. Its position in some countries has not been helped by the fact that the issue of local finances tends to be a sensitive and controversial political matter, which makes it all the more difficult to raise local revenues. This, in turn, brings us back to the point that it is state or central government which determines the taxes to be available, and that it is largely beyond the power of local government to adapt its revenue raising capacities to changing circumstances. Consequently, it does not find it easy to avoid the political consequences of visible taxes, a fact of great importance for the local government systems which rely upon such taxes for a significant proportion of local revenues.

Once again, it would be unfair and inaccurate to concentrate exclusively upon the powerlessness of local government, for it is not a helpless victim of fate. On the contrary it has contributed to the situation in a thousand different ways; by making electioneering promises, by pressing central government for more powers and more money, by voluntarily lifting standards for services, by building bigger and more costly municipal facilities, by employing larger numbers of highly trained and expensive professionals, and, in general, by planning steady improvements over the past few decades in its own level of performance. The point remains, however, that local government is only one part of a large complexity of political forces. Its willingness to increase its expenditure and to minimize its income taxes, fees, and charges, is understandable when placed in the broader context of political movements and trends which were widespread throughout the four quarters of the globe in the two decades stretching approximately from 1955 to 1975.

Responses to the resource squeeze

A brief review of the four major sets of constraints on local government suggests that room for financial manoeuvre is relatively restricted, at least by comparison with private business and with higher levels of government. There are, however, some approaches to the problem of balancing the books which should be considered. They are:

1. Reducing expenditure.
2. The transfer of services to a higher level of government.
3. The transfer of services to the private sector.
4. Raising more money from fees and charges.
5. Profit making activities.
6. A larger share of better taxes.
7. Larger central government grants.
8. Going further into debt.

The rest of the chapter will examine the main attractions and drawbacks of these modes of adaption. Since none is necessarily incompatible with any other, and all may be combined at the same time, the order in which they are taken is of no great significance.

1. Reducing expenditure

The most obvious response to high and increasing levels of expenditure is to look for ways of cutting expenditure, if possible without reducing services. This approach has a good deal of attraction for many members of the general public who are firmly of the opinion that a large proportion of rising costs is attributable to nothing more complicated than waste and profligacy. The view is usually supported by a variety of examples which are variations on three or four themes.

a. *An excess of lazy bureaucrats*. The favourite bête noire of the general public is the bureaucrat who spends most of his time doing nothing in particular, with a whole office full of colleagues to help him. One of the most common stereotypes of the public sector is that it is grossly overstaffed and needs energetic pruning. Hard evidence for this point of view, however, is difficult to find. In the first place, there are as many, if not more, bureaucrats (i.e. office workers) in the private sector as in the public, and in the second their work rate and productivity is notoriously difficult to measure or compare. Consequently, statements about overstaffing and laziness are very largely a matter of opinion, prejudice, and popular myth.
b. *Wastefulness*. Letters to newspapers, bar-room discussions, and questions at public meetings show that many people are convinced that government departments of all kinds are wasteful and inefficient. Evidence to support the view often includes examples of poor planning and building, inefficiency in organizing and providing services, and bureaucratic muddle and indecision. Local government, like any other organization, especially large ones, has its fair share of mistakes and needless costs, but once again, there is no hard evidence that its record is worse than the average for either

public or private enterprises of any kind. Popular beliefs about the matter sometimes run strong, but there is no hard substance to confirm or deny them.

c. *Profligacy*. In some countries local government officials are sometimes accused of spending large quantities of public money on such things as limousines and banquets for officials, trips abroad for spurious purposes, and all manner of luxuries in the town hall. While there may be occasional substance to such accusations, it is clear that profligacy on even a huge scale would not account for more than a relatively minute proportion of total spending. In any case it seems clear that the 'expenses' charged by local government officials are no more than a small fraction of those commonly charged by executives in private industry.

d. *Spending other people's money*. Local government is cavalier and spendthrift, so it is said, because it spends other people's money. The argument is true, but fails to carry any explanatory weight worth mentioning simply because it overlooks the fact that the great majority of businessmen also spend other people's money. Indeed, there is probably some truth in the suggestion that local authorities are so conscious of spending other people's money, and are reminded of this with such frequency, that they are especially careful as a result.

The plain and simple fact, unacceptable though it may be to whole sections of the population in some countries, is that there is no hard evidence to suggest that local expenditure has been borne up on a rising tide of wastefulness, laziness, and lavish spending. One has only to look at a few of the figures in earlier chapters of this book to realise why local spending has risen so steeply in the post-war period. In fact, given such things as the massive increase in school children, the sharp rise in interest rates, the progressive expansion of the old and retired population, and accumulation of minimum standards legislation, it is really rather remarkable that local spending has not risen harder and faster.

What this amounts to, in effect, is the argument that though local government, like any other form of human organization, makes mistakes, and spends money needlessly, this is not a root cause of rising expenditure. Local government activity has increased in volume and price, because modern society, through a complex network of social, economic, and political forces, plus a wide range of government laws, has required it to do so. Wastefulness and profligacy of one kind or another is no more than a marginal consideration, and only relatively small amounts are likely to be saved by hunting it down. This does not mean that it is not worth doing, but it would be wasteful both in this work and in the real world to spend much time on it. It is more important, by far, to look at the real problems and to assess the merits of strategies which stand a good chance of having a major impact.

An important implication of all this is that cuts in local spending of any magnitude are likely to have an immediate impact upon the quality of public services. And if, as quite often happens, the cuts bite into the services for the poorest and weakest sections of society, because they are the least able to protect themselves, then the loss of amenity may affect the quality of their lives in quite a serious manner. It ought not to be assumed that public expenditure cuts cause the cream to be skimmed off the least essential services, or that they provoke cuts in services for those who are best placed to suffer the loss; on the contrary, those who most need public services — the poor, the old, the very young, and the ill — are likely to endure the worst effects, if only because they are often in the worst position to defend their interests.

On the other hand, local government is likely to be caught in a dilemma, for if it cuts services for the wealthier and better organized sections of society, it is likely to feel the sting of pressure group backlash. If, as has been suggested in earlier chapters, local government is sensitive to the pressures brought to bear by the more articulate and better organized sections of modern society, then local officials are likely to compromise or capitulate, and then renew their search for services to cut. If they do not actually start off by reducing some of the services designed for those whose need is greatest, they are likely to turn to them after a few political skirmishes with influential organizations armed with loud barks and painful bites.

2. The transfer of services to higher levels of government

If it is difficult to make cuts without reducing service quality, and no less difficult to make cuts which result in the least possible injustice to the old, the young, and the weak, then perhaps the solution is to transfer some of the most expensive local services to higher levels of government. This might be done on the grounds that state or national government has a broader, and often more satisfactory tax base, and might be able to absorb services which are a considerable financial burden to local government without too much difficulty. It may not be necessary to transfer a whole service, but only a part of it, such as, for example, the salaries and wages of teachers and other school staff. This sort of arrangement seems to work well in some countries and it might well reduce the financial problems of local government to more manageable proportions.

Although the solution may have its attractions at first glance, it also has its problems. In the first place, it obviously has to meet with the agreement of central government and this may be difficult to get. The aim of some governing parties in Western society is to force down public expenditure, in which case they are unlikely to favour a simple transfer of functions between levels of government. In the second place, even if such a transfer were acceptable, it would give central government power over a wider range of public functions, and there is a strong school of thought in many Western societies which opposes such centralization on the grounds that the erosion of local autonomy and democracy has already gone too far. In the third place, local government would have to ensure that its income was not reduced by the exact cost of the service(s) which had been transferred upwards, or else it would wind up in the position of having its responsibilities and power reduced, with no improvement in its financial circumstances — it would be left with its financial problem, but on a slightly smaller scale.

3. Transferring services to the private sector

While higher levels of government may be unwilling to take over the responsibility for local services, or for parts of them, there is always the possibility of moving some functions out of the public domain and into the private sector. Such a move also requires central government permission if it involves services for which local government has a statutory responsibility, but it may be viewed favourably by some governments of a right wing and laissez-faire persuasion. Many people would agree that certain types of amenities and services cannot and ought not to be provided by market enterprises, but there are others which, it might be argued, are likely to be as well, or better, provided by private firms than public agencies. In West Germany, slaughterhouses, refuse collection, and local authority computer services have recently been transferred to private enterprise by some municipalities. The privatization of computer services has considerable merits in that it enables a number of authorities to share the same capital intensive and highly skilled technology.

But privatization also has its failings. If the service is relatively costless (or if it actually breaks even, or makes a profit), local government is unlikely to hive it off for financial reasons, but if it makes a loss, then private enterprise is unlikely to be interested in it. In certain circumstances private enterprise may be inclined to take over a service in order to shed the loss-making parts and concentrate on the profit-making ones, but this may be unacceptable if it means that some people are deprived of important services. Refuse may be collected in affluent areas which can afford it, but not in poorer ones, thus creating a public health hazard. Buses may run on profit-making routes, but not on others, thus tending to isolate some of those without private transport from their doctors or their schools. The main objection to transferring services to the private sector, however, is the simple one that it would make little difference to the general scale of local government costs. The largest and most expensive services are generally concerned with education, welfare, and a combination of such things as general administration, health, police, town planning, and various youth services. These are precisely the sorts of services which are least amenable to privatization. Even if it made good economic and political sense to sell such things as street cleaning, leisure and sports services, and refuse collection to private industry, this would not make a really large impact on the strength of the resource squeeze, although it might be argued that every little would help.

4. Raising more money from fees and charges

The three approaches to reducing the resource squeeze discussed so far deal with changes in the number and scale of service functions, and are designed to reduce the overall size of the local government bill. Another set of approaches concentrates on ways of increasing local authority income so that financial capacities are brought more into line with functional responsibilities. Among these may be numbered the option of increasing the total amount of money raised from fees and charges, either by introducing charges for services which are currently free, or by raising the level of existing charges. Since flat rate charges are regressive (that is, the poor pay a higher porportion of their income for the same service as the rich), such charges are unlikely to be politically acceptable to those who pay proportionately more, or to those who are concerned about achieving a greater degree of social and economic justice in society. The possibility of introducing a wide range of small charges which might be acceptable on social justice grounds, may also be ruled out on economic grounds, since they are likely to be expensive to collect.

One way round these problems is to introduce selective charges which are imposed upon some people but not on others. Once again there are administrative, social, and economic reasons for not departing from the universal principle of either charging nobody for the service, or of charging everybody the same price. Selectivity tends to introduce a cumbersome administrative machinery of official forms, offices, claims, appeals, and rebates; it may possibly introduce invidious social distinctions which are resented by lower income groups; and it may be more expensive to charge different rates, than to charge everybody the same, low rate.

Chapter 7 of this study shows that some countries (Norway, the UK and West Germany) could increase their total income by a not insignificant amount if they increased their present fees and charges by, say, 40 or 50 percent. However, the chapter also shows that this method of increasing income has provoked fierce political resistance in Italy and the UK, with the result that local politicians are careful, in these two countries at least, to proceed gently. Political resistance is based, of course, upon the idea that public services should either be cheap or free because they are believed to be essential to the welfare of the population using them. This is certainly true so far as education, certain kinds of housing, social welfare, and a variety of other local services is concerned, but there seem to be some such as car parks, for example, which do not fall into this category, and for which economic prices might reasonably be charged. The list of appropriate services is not long, however, and insofar as it mainly includes such items as markets, slaughterhouses, airports, some forms of transport and housing, and harbours, ports, and piers, it is unlikely to be much of a money-spinner.

5. Profit making activities

The preceding section leads naturally to another possibility which involves local authorities in a variety of profit making activities. For example, Norwegian municipalities run cinemas, and make a useful surplus which contributes towards the costs of other services; in America, some of the states have a monopoly of liquor sales. In general, however, a state monopoly of profit making activities is not allowed on the grounds that such services should be left to the free market. Yet there seems to be no reason why local authorities should not be allowed to make a profit on a small range of goods and services, particularly where, as in the case of some forms of gambling, there are sound reasons for public control. If local government is to be permitted, or encouraged, to charge fees which fall short of the cost price for necessities such as housing and transport, why should it not charge higher than cost prices for non-essentials, such as casinos and other forms of gambling, which may be better run by public agencies in any case?

6. A larger share of better taxes

More important, by far, than profit making activities, is the need in some countries to make local revenue raising capacities consonant with the scale of financial responsibilities. The Scandinavian nations in this survey have managed to do so by allowing their municipalities a local income tax, and Italy and West Germany have moved in this direction in recent years. Moreover, a thorough inquiry into local government finances in the UK (the Layfield Report) has also made an exceedingly strong case for the introduction of a local income tax. The report's conclusions in this respect are strongly supported by the findings of the present survey which show that local government systems with an income tax at their disposal have the least severe financial problems. There can be no doubt that one of the most important policy implications of the survey is the importance of a local income tax as the basis for healthy local authority finances.

Local income tax on a small scale will not necessarily solve the worst crisis. New York City, for example, introduced an income tax in 1967, and by 1973/4 it accounted for 12.4% of locally derived tax revenues. At the same time, the city's property tax contributed 56% of the total, a fact which underlines the inadequacy of property taxes as a source of income. Nevertheless, New York finances would almost certainly have been even more critical without an income tax. So far as one can judge from international experience, the introduction of a local income tax may not solve a full-blooded crisis once it has developed, but it can be a powerful force which prevents it developing in the first place.

Whatever its attractions from the revenue raising point of view, a local income tax has a mixed political appeal. On the one hand, it will generally give local authorities more control over their own affairs and, hence, will tend to improve the quality of local democracy by making local authorities more responsible for their taxing and spending policies. This may be thought a considerable asset by those who are concerned with the questions of democracy and accountability in government. On the other hand, their views contrast strongly with those of some central governments which are highly reluctant to grant their junior partners in the municipalities a share of the best taxes. Among the major Western European nations, only in Denmark, Norway, Sweden, and Switzerland does local government raise a third or more of its total income from income taxes. In Austria, Belgium, France, Luxembourg, The Netherlands, Turkey, and the UK, local authorities are either not allowed to levy an income tax, or else are limited to a small share of it. It is argued in some of these countries that a local income tax would make planning and controlling the national economy more difficult, even impossible. Whatever truth lies in this speculation so far as some countries are concerned, it must be pointed out that Denmark, Sweden, Norway, and Switzerland have relatively strong economies by contemporary standards and seem to suffer little, if at all, from their local income taxes.

Another argument which may be used against a local income tax is that although it may help to increase the power of local authorities over their own affairs, it tends to reduce the accountability of taxing authorities to their tax paying citizens. This is because the buoyancy and relative invisibility of income taxes in many countries means that politicians have to work less hard to justify their taxes to the general public. Property taxes, in contrast, are one of the most accountable forms of taxation yet devised by modern government, and are thus a powerful obstacle to the revenue raising aspirations of politicians. True though this is, we must be careful not to apply double standards to local and central government. There is no obvious reason for allowing central government the lion's share of relatively invisible and buoyant taxes, while insisting that local government should stick to the more accountable taxes. What is sauce for the goose is sauce for the gander, and as long as income tax is levied, local government has every right to a share of it.

7. Larger central government grants

Table 1.3 shows that central government grants have increased appreciably as a percentage of gross local income in five of the six countries in the survey — West Germany is the single exception where, ever since 1950, grants have stayed constant at 27%. An increase in grants as a response to the local resource squeeze can be defended on the grounds that it allows local authorities to retain their full range of functions while, at the same time, easing local financial problems. Besides this, central government may encourage the trend since it increases its control of local government finances which, in their turn, form a significant part of the national economy. It also permits central government to respond to pressures from the general public and local authorities for more public services, while allowing it to keep its distance from the delicate political and administrative tasks of actually delivering services. Lastly, on the positive side, central grants make it possible to redistribute money between areas in accordance with the requirements of equality and social justice.

At the same time, the familiar complaint against increasing grants is that they enhance the capacity for the centralized control of society. In other words, if it is true that 'He who pays the piper, calls the tune', then increasing grants simply pave the way for a still more centralized state in which local authorities are progressively reduced to the role of administrative outposts of central departments. In effect, then, central government is attracted to grants, and local authorities are often opposed to them in principle, for the reason that they can easily lead to central control. However, local authorities with inadequate resources of their own may have little choice but to accept larger and larger grants. This leads to a second point that the argument about using grants to redistribute resources may be more than a little hollow, if the huge amounts transferred from central to local government are less concerned with distribution than with simply shoring up shaky local finances. That is, large grants may have only a small redistributive element, if their main purpose is to fill gaping holes in the whole system of local finances. Small grants in a system which is basically very healthy, may have a much larger redistributive element. In short, the size of the grant should not be confused with the extent to which it is redistributive.

8. Going futher into debt

The strategy of going into debt in order to reduce the severity of the resource squeeze is frequently employed because of its short term, and some of its long term benefits. It enables local authorities to avoid the disadvantages of central government grants, and in inflationary periods, it may make a good deal of financial sense to borrow heavily, even if this provokes something of a cash flow problem in the short run. There are also some good reasons for borrowing in order to finance capital expenditure: capital projects have a value lasting for more than a single financial year, and it therefore makes sense to spread the cost over a period of years; capital projects benefit future as well as present taxpayers, and they should bear a share of the costs, therefore; and the 'lumpiness' of capital expenditure may be smoothed out by spreading costs over the years.

Yet loans carry interest payments, and these have risen steeply in the past decade of high inflation. Consequently, debts charges have also increased as a proportion of total expenditure in countries where local authorities have a large borrowing requirement. An intensified resource squeeze in these countries could result in a further round of borrowing in order to service or pay off old debts, and this could lead to a dangerous escalation of more borrowing and more debt charges, followed, sooner or later, by a collapse of credit worthiness. This possibility is reduced in many countries by the fact that central government regulates many aspects of local borrowing, and by the fact that local authorities tend to owe a high proportion of their debts to central government which is unlikely to let local authorities approach the point of bankruptcy. Nevertheless, large scale debts are not a satisfactory way of solving financial problems because they generate their own short term problems, which may extend into the long term, and because they reduce the amount of money for items of current expenditure, which, in turn, limits the possibility of using current revenues for capital projects. The force of circumstances may oblige local authorities to go further into debt, but it is not the most satisfactory response to the resource squeeze.

Big cities, central government, and the Cinderella syndrome

Before concluding this work, three points of a very general nature should be made about the policy implications of its findings. The first is that central governments should recognise the special circumstances of big cities when they think about the problems of financing local government. Some of these circumstances are only vaguely recognised, while others are barely recognised at all, although they seem to have a strong and direct impact on urban finances in all six of the nations covered in this study. It is not that the biggest cities suffer from diseconomies of scale in service provision, for this tendency has yet to be satisfactorily demonstrated for a wide range of services and facilities. Rather it is that urban life calls for all manner of public provisions which are either less urgent, or entirely absent, or impossibly expensive to provide in rural and small town authorities. The larger the city, and the more important its place in the national and international system of cities, the greater its financial requirements.

It is not necessary to summarize the conclusions of Chapter 8, but it is worth emphasizing that a recognition of the special financial needs of large cities and metropolitan areas means either making it possible for them to raise revenues which are concomitant with the depth and breadth of their service provision, or else increasing the size of their grants. This might be done by building in big city factors into the various formulas and procedures for distributing central government grants to local government. If neither course of action is followed, the list of cities in Western Europe and elsewhere which run into severe financial problems is likely to increase at a rapid pace, and for reasons which are largely, but not wholly, beyond the control of the cities themselves.

This leads into the second general point which is that higher levels of government, especially national government, play such an enormously important role in the political economy of local government that it is not too much of an exaggeration to suggest that a large part of the financial problems which beset the localities are attributable not to their own policies and actions, but, on the contrary, to the laws enacted and the policies pursued by central government. An institution which is largely unable to determine what services and facilities it will provide for what sections of the population, and which is bound by powerful constraints when it comes to deciding how to finance these services, cannot be held primarily responsible for a tendency for expenditure to outstrip income. In this respect, one of the principal conclusions to come out of this comparative survey of six Western European nations is that the political economy of local government is so completely intertwined, and so strongly influenced or determined by central government action, that any analysis of the former's problems will inevitably lead to the door of the latter. To put it in more direct and simple terms, central government must generally carry at least as much of the praise or blame as local government for the state of local finances. The local fiscal crisis, where it exists, is not local at all; it is central-local.

In this respect, local government in some countries is very much the poor and junior partner in a decidedly unequal relationship. It has traditionally provided most of the dull and humdrum services, such as water, sewerage, refuse disposal, and roads, which are easily overlooked, but which are entirely necessary for modern civilized life. It has responsibility for a large, if not the largest part of the more expensive services such as education, housing, and welfare. And more recently, it has pioneered many exciting and innovative services such as environmental control, planning, leisure facilities, and consumer protection, as well as developing new ways of delivering traditional community services. In spite of all this it remains the Cinderella of the system of government in many countries. There are exceptions, but these serve to highlight its generally rather disdainful treatment in other nations. This is not only socially and politically unreasonable, it is also likely to precipitate increasingly acute financial problems which threaten the very basis of modern government and society. It is time Cinderella went to the ball.

Index

2